FL   3.24

G000071082

TREES AND FRUITS OF SOUTHEAST ASIA

An Illustrated Field Guide

Michael Jensen

Orchid Press
Bangkok

TREES AND FRUITS OF SOUTHEAST ASIA.
An Illustrated Field Guide
Michael Jensen

First published: 1995
by FAO Regional Office for Asia and the Pacific (RAP)
Orchid Guides edition: 2001

Orchid Press
P. O. Box 19,
Yuttitham Post Office
Bangkok 10907, Thailand

ISBN 974-8304-67-1

CONTENTS

INTRODUCTION

The work for this field guide started back in 1994 when I myself was looking for a practical guide to cultivated trees. I needed this to assist me in my work as an agro-forestry specialist in the FAO Regional Office for Asia and the Pacific, especially during field trips. However, I soon realized that the information I was looking for was neither available in any single publication, nor in a practical format. In agreement with the forestry officer, Mr Masakazu Kashio, I therefore decided that it would be useful to produce such a book myself. This turned out to be quite a cumbersome task. The collection of information, including more than 1000 photographs, the production of about 100 colour plates and the preparation of the manuscript and layout lasted almost two years, and FAO kindly published the material in 1995.

Much of the material for the book was collected on numerous trips to most of the countries of the Southeast Asia region, and I am grateful to FAO for the opportunity to work in the region and learn about the botany and plant life of this part of the world.

The aim of this book has been to provide a popular and practical field guide for non-expert botanist to the identification and use of commonly cultivated trees in Southeast Asia. The book should be of particular interest to foresters, agronomists, economists, sociologists, ecologists, extension workers, students and others involved in rural development work as well as travellers seeking to explore the wealth of tropical crops. It is my hope that this book will lead to a greater appreciation of a much wider variety of tree crops and to the increased planting of these species.

The original manuscript has been revised thoroughly and a number of changes have been made to produce a pleasing and practical layout. A calendar has been added describing the main fruiting seasons of particular tree crops in the region.

During the process numerous people – too many to be mentioned here – have provided invaluable help for which I am very grateful. However, I would like to express my sincere thanks to Mr Masakazu Kashio, FAO Regional Forest Resources Officer. Without his support, encouragement and technical comments this work would not have been possible.

Copenhagen, July 2000

Michael Jensen
Tropical Biologist

HOW TO USE THIS FIELD GUIDE

This book is designed to enable the identification of the most common trees that are likely to be encountered in the rural areas of Southeast Asia, including the following countries: Burma, Lao PDR, Thailand, Cambodia, Vietnam, China (southern part), Malaysia, Singapore, Indonesia, Brunei and the Philippines. The guide is not intended to be comprehensive – users will certainly encounter trees that are not included in this guide, including some of the thousands of wild tree species of the region, semi-wild species and species of very limited distribution. Rather, the tree species selected for this field guide are those trees that are most widely cultivated on and around farms, in plantations and along roads and canals within the tropical or subtropical areas of at least one of the countries of Southeast Asia. Species that are found only in very dry areas, deserts or at altitudes above 2,000 metres, have not been included.

Each tree species is illustrated using colour plates, showing the tree habit, structure of leaves, flowers, fruit and bark and other characteristic features. Opposite to this plate species synonyms, local names, major uses, ecology and distribution, including a distribution map for some species, are described. The key characteristics for identification are highlighted for quick reference. For the benefit of readers with further interest in breeding, propagation, management or use, key references are provided.

The species included in the guide are first grouped according to their overall taxonomic relationship. Within these groupings species are presented in alphabetical order. An index of scientific as well as common and local names can be found at the end of the guide. To ease the process of identification, a key has been included. The key avoids the traditional extensive use of flower characteristics, since flowers are often not readily available. Users, however, should recognize that such a simple key may not yield successful results in all cases. Users may have to resort to the individual species description in order to properly identify species.

It is important to realize that many trees show great variability compared to standard characteristics as a result of genetic variation and differences in local growing conditions.

If consultation with experts is needed to identify species, plant material may be collected and preserved using simple pressing and drying techniques. Such sampling would normally be restricted to leaves and flowers. These materials can be preserved by placing them between newspaper sheets or other paper and pressing them with some books or other heavy flat objects for several hours. If a more lasting result is needed, additional heat and air circulation must be provided and the drying period extended to 24 hours.

Always be sure
not to damage trees fatally when collecting samples.

INTRODUCTION TO TERMINOLOGY

Although technical language has been kept to a minimum in this field guide, some terms that have been used to describe species may be unfamiliar to some users. These terms are defined through illustrations in this section.

LEAVES

Arrangement of leaves:

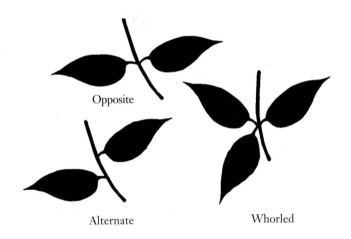

Opposite

Alternate

Whorled

Leaf structures:

Simple

Palmately compound

Even pinnately
compound

Odd-pinnately
compound

Bipinnately compound

Leaf shapes:

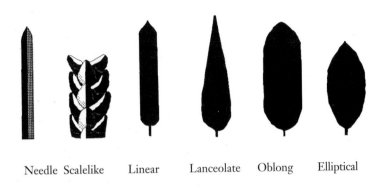

Needle Scalelike   Linear   Lanceolate   Oblong   Elliptical

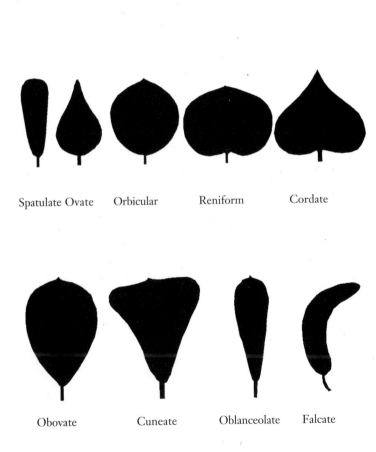

Spatulate Ovate   Orbicular   Reniform   Cordate

Obovate   Cuneate   Oblanceolate   Falcate

Leaf margins:

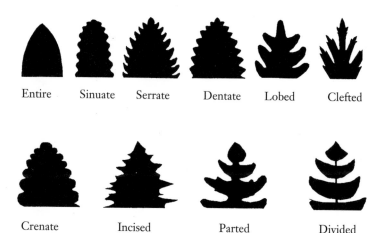

Entire Sinuate Serrate Dentate Lobed Clefted

Crenate Incised Parted Divided

Leaf tips:

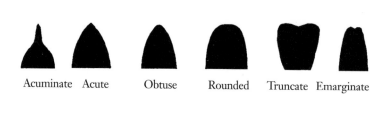

Acuminate Acute Obtuse Rounded Truncate Emarginate

Leaf bases:

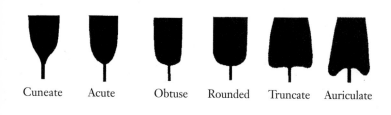

Cuneate Acute Obtuse Rounded Truncate Auriculate

Leaf venation:

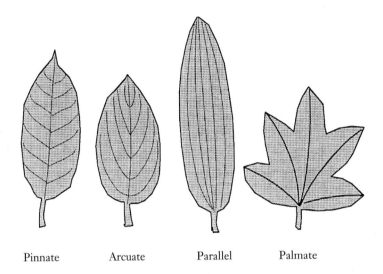

Pinnate   Arcuate   Parallel   Palmate

FLOWERS

Flowers are the reproductive organs of plants and their characteristics are often important for plant identification in traditional flora. Flower characteristics define a plant's placement in the taxonomic system. Unfortunately, many trees only flower once a year or even more rarely, hence the flowers are often not available when needed for identification. In this field guide emphasis has therefore been given to features of leaves, bark and other vegetative characters. However, when flowers are available they can provide valuable clues to the identification of a tree.

Flower structure:

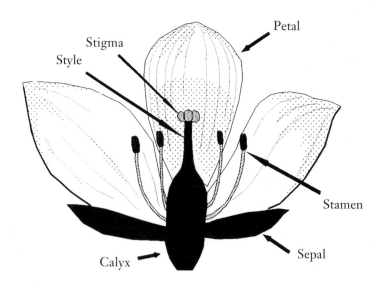

Flower arrangement (or inflorescence):

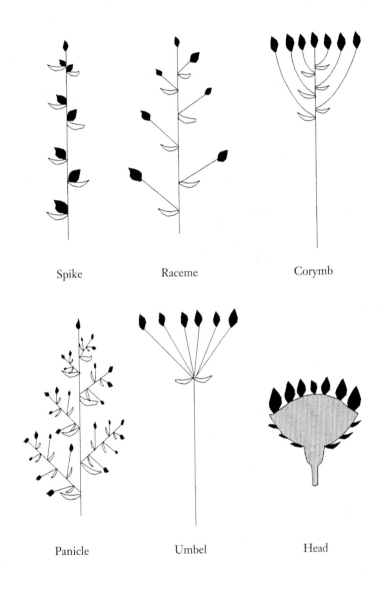

Spike   Raceme   Corymb

Panicle   Umbel   Head

FRUITS

Common types of fruit:

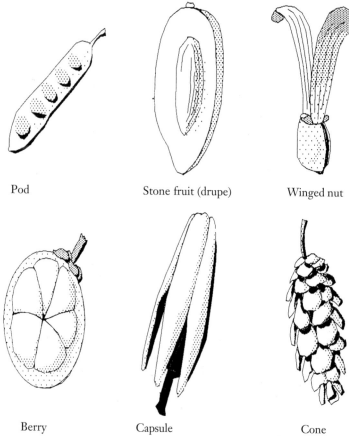

Pod

Stone fruit (drupe)

Winged nut

Berry

Capsule

Cone

Different fruit shapes:

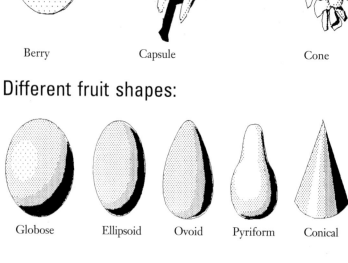

Globose

Ellipsoid

Ovoid

Pyriform

Conical

BARK, BOLE and BRANCHES

Although the appearance of a tree's bark can often vary within the same species between young and old trees, between trunk and branches, and sometimes between individuals growing under different conditions, most tree species still have some prevailing characteristic features of the bark that can help identification. The true appearance of the bark can often be obscured by lichens, mosses or other vegetation, particularly on old trees. The colour, smell or even taste of the inner bark may be a characteristic feature as well, but restraint should be shown in cutting the bark to check these, since such open wounds may make the tree susceptible to diseases.

The growth pattern of trunk and branches is often characteristic for a species as well. Some species develop a straight bole but other species may be crooked or twisted. The latter may be particularly pronounced under harsh growing conditions. Some trees branch near the base, whereas others have the first branches high up the trunk. Moreover the same tree may have different branching patterns depending on the density of competing vegetation, with branches generally starting lower in more open habitats. Similarly the crown of most trees will be more narrow in dense vegetation, whereas other trees of the same species growing in open conditions may develop a much wider crown. In some trees, the branches appear in characteristic whorls on the trunk. On others, branches have a horizontal orientation, curve upwards, hang down, or show other characteristic features which are important in helping to identify them.

KEY TO TREE IDENTIFICATION

Proceed step by step through the key, each time choosing the closest match of two or more options. Since this is only a selection of species, do a final check of your plant with the species description and illustration itself.

Note: This guide is strictly limited to domesticated trees. Most of these have many wild relatives with some similar characteristics, but in addition there are thousands of other species not covered by this key. To bring this field guide to a natural forest and expect to use it for general botanical identification will thus only lead to confusion and misinterpretations.

MAJOR GROUPS:

I. CONIFERS and CASUARINAS
Branched tree with leaves modified to needles or scales (Agathis with normal leaves), no colorful flowers, fruits are cones.

II. BAMBOOS
Multistemmed, erect (except a few climbing forms), branches from internodes, flowers rare.

III. PALMS and BANANAS
Unbranched erect (or climbing) stem with large leaves and flower stands from centre of crown.

IV. BROADLEAVED TREES
Branched shrub or tree with ordinary leaves.

I. CONIFERS and CASUARINAS

1. *Needles*

1.1 Needles in bundles of 2 .... *Pinus merkusii* 33
1.2 Needles mostly in bundles of 3
a. White-powdered branchlets; cones in groups .... *Pinus kesiya* 31
b. Young twigs orange-brown; cones single .... *Pinus caribaea* 29

2. *Scales*

2.1 Bark dark, reddish-brown to black .... *Araucaria* 25
2.2 Bark light grey-brown .... *Casuarina* 27

3. *Parallel nerved thick leaves* .... *Agathis* 23

II. BAMBOOS

Bamboo spp. 35

III. PALMS and BANANAS

1. *Soft, green stem* .... Bananas (Musa spp.) 45

2. *Woody stem*

2.1 Fan-shaped leaves. .... *Borassus* 39
2.2 Feather-shaped leaves
a. Leaves 1-1.5 m long; stem smooth, slender .... *Areca* 37
b. Leaves 4-5 m long, fruits large .... *Cocos* 41
c. Leaves to 7.5 m long, stem rugged .... *Elaeis* 43

3. *Climbing, flexible, thorny stem* .... *Rattans* 47

IV. BROADLEAVED TREES
Leaf types:

a	b	c	d	e

Palmate	Trifoliate	Opposite single	Pinnate	Alternate single
page 14	page 14	page 15	page 15	page 17

IV-a: Palmate leaves

1.Palmately compound leaves
  1.1 Leaves in whorls of 5-8, not truly palmate; flowers small, greenish-yellow; no spines .... *Alstonia* 61
  1.2 3-5 leaflets; flowers small, bluish; no spines Vitex 207
  1.3 5-7 leaflets; flowers large, red; spiny .... *Bombax* 81
  1.4 5-11 leaflets; flowers medium, white; spiny *Ceiba* 95
2.Single large palmate leaves; often unbranched Carica 89

IV-b: Trifoliate leaves

*1.Leaflets large, thin and heart-shaped or broadly ovate; trunk thorny; flowers large, orange or red*Erythrina 115
2.Leaflets small, lance-shaped; shrub .... Cajanus 85

3.Leaflets elliptic to ovate
  3.1 Leaflets 4-26 cm long, shiny above, hairy below, yellow-red before falling off; bark smooth, pinkish *Sandoricum*183
  3.2 Leaflets 4-50 cm; bark pale brown to dark brown; fruit 3-lobedcapsule .... *Hevea* 135
  3.3 Leaflets to 7.5 cm long; old branches thorny*Aegle 55*

IV-c: Opposite leaves

1.Leaves 15-38 cm long

1.1 Lance-shaped leaves .... *Syzygium jambos* 195

1.2 Heart-shaped leaves .... *Gmelina* 129

1.3 Obovate leaves

   1.3.1 Medium-sized; branches horizontal,
in whorls .... *Terminalia* 203

   1.3.2 Small; crooked trunk; irregular crown
.... *Syzygium aqueum* 191

   1.3.3 Medium-sized; straight; irregular crown
.... *Syzygium cumini* 193

1.4 Elliptic or oblong leaves

   1.4.1 Branches in whorls; small tree; secondary
nerves bent and joining .... *Gnetum* 131

   1.4.2 Branches not in whorls

   a. Straight trunk; medium-sized tree

   - Leaves to 38 cm long; flowers red
.... *Syzygium malac.* 197

   - Leaves to 25 cm long; flowers yellow-green
.... *Garcinia* 125

   - Flowers purplish .... *Lagerstroemia speciosa* 139

   b. Crooked trunk; small tree
.... *Syzygium samarangense* 191

   c. Shrub or small tree .... *Coffea canephora* 105

2.Leaves 1-15 cm long

2.1 Medium to very large tree; straight trunk

   2.1.1 Very large; stem smooth, brightly colored; leaves
ovate to lanceolate .... *Eucalyptus deglupta* 119

   2.1.2 Large; bark grey and orange; leaves asymmetric,
ovate or obovate; flowers only one, white petal
.... *Intsia* 137

2.2 Shrub to small, low-branching tree

   2.2.1 Small tree; bark green to red-brown,
peeling off .... *Psidium* 177

   2.2.2 Spiny bush/small tree; leaves small,
lanceolate .... *Punica* 181

   2.2.3 Shrub; horizontal branches; leaves oval to
elliptical,margin often undulating
.... *Coffea arabica* 105

IV-d: Leaves pinnate, bipinnate or tripinnate

1. Leaflets 5-25 mm long

2. Leaflets 20-60 mm long

3. Leaflets 50-250 mm long

      * 2-5 pairs of entire leaflets, 3-16 cm long .... *Litchi* 145

      * 4-10 pairs of leaflets, 5-25 cm long, sometimes crenate
        or serrated .... *Spondias cytherea* 187

    b. Leaflets ovate-oblong

      * Small tree; numerous large, yellow flowers; fruit long
        cylindrical pod .... *Cassia fistula* 91

      * Medium to large tree; buttresses; fruit large roundish
        5-valved capsule .... *Swietenia* (*macroph.*) 189

    c. Leaflets ovate to obovate, hairy below .... *Nephelium* 165

3.2 Leaves odd-pinnate (with single terminal leaflet)

3.2.1 Leaflets alternate

    a. 6-9 leaflets, 9-21 cm long .... *Lansium* 141

    b. 7-11 leaflets, 5-10 cm long .... *Pterocarpus* 179

    3.2.2 Leaflets opposite

    a. 2-6 pairs of elliptic to ovate leaflets .... *Averrhoa car.* 73

    b. 7-19 pairs of ovate leaflets .... *Averrhoa bilimbi* 73

IV-e: Alternate single leaves

1.Leaves with parallel nerves

1.1 leaves and/or stalks hairy .... *Ziziphus* 209

1.2 leaves without hairs, fruits are pods

    1.2.1 Stem straight; leaves to 25 cm long;
          flowers white ...... *Acacia mangium* 53

    1.2.2 Stem sometimes multi-stemmed and/or
          crooked; leaves narrow, 5-18 cm long;
          flowers yellow .... *Acacia auriculiformis* 49

2.Leaves with toothed edge

2.1 Leaves and/or flower stands hairy
                .... *Muntingia* 161

2.2 Leaves smooth

    2.2.1 Leaves oblong to lanceolate, in whorls of 3
          .... *Macadamia* 147

    2.2.2 Leaves ovate, sometimes lobed .... *Morus* 159

3.Winged leaf stalks; translucent spots in leaves; spiny branches

3.1 Leaf stalk narrowly winged or margined

    3.1.1 Usually very spiny, leaves ovate to
          elliptic, fruit flesh greenish,very sour
          .... *Citrus aurantiifolia* 99

    3.1.2 Sometimes spiny, leaves ovate to lanceolate, fruit
          flesh orange, sweet .... *Citrus reticulata* 103

3.2 Leaf stalk broadly winged
3.2.1 Young parts soft-haired; +/- long spines; wings to 7 cm wide; fruit smooth, to 30 cm diameter, sweet .... *Citrus grandis* 101
3.2.2 Spines small, wings to 4.5 cm wide; fruit with bumpy skin, to 7 cm diameter, very acid .... *Citrus hystrix* 99

4.Leaves lobed
4.1 Leaves 5-7 cm long, toothed
.... *Morus* 159
4.2 Leaves 20-60 cm long, deeply pinnately .....
lobed ....*Artocarpus altilis* 67
4.3 Leaves 5-25 cm long, 1-2 lobes on young plants
................................*Artocarpus heterophyllus* 69
4.4 Leaves fernlike, 9-21 pairs of leaflets with deep
narrow lobes.. *Grevillea* 133

5.Leaves very large, to 60 cm long and 40 cm wide
5.1 Leaves deeply pinnately lobed
...................................*Artocarpus altilis* 67
5.2 Leaves entire .... *Tectona* 201
6.Leaves have none of the above features

Leaf shape

Heart-shaped Oblong Obovate Lanceolate Ovate Elliptic

6.1	6.2	6.3	6.4	6.5	6.6

6.1 Leaves heart-shaped to ovate; bark green to red; rust colored scales on young twigs; flowers large, pink or white.. *Bixa* 79
6.2 Leaves oblong
6.2.1 Shrub/small tree; branches in whorls; leaves 15-50 cm long .... *Theobroma* 205
6.2.2 Medium-sized tree; branchlets brown-haired; leaves 5-16 cm long, rust red below ...... *Chrysophyllum* 97
6.2.3 Small to medium-sized tree; branches often drooping; leaves with pleasant smell if crushed .... *Persea* 171
6.3 Leaves obovate
6.3.1 Leaves and/or branchlets with brown or yellow-red hairs.

a. Leaves rust red below, 5-16 cm long;

    branchlets brown-haired .... *Chrysophyllum* 97

b. Leaves 5-25 cm long, brown-haired .... *Artocarpus integer* 71

6.3.2 Leaves and branchlets without brown or yellow-red hairs

a. Flowers/fruits on twigs
- Leaves silky white below .... *Manilkara kaukii* 153
- Leaves with prominent midrib and veins .... *Anacardium* 63

b. Flowers/fruits on trunk/large branches
- Leaves glandular; fruits small, round .... *Baccaurea racemosa* 77
- Fruits very large, irregular .... *Artocarpus heterophyllus* 69

6.4 Lance-shaped leaves

6.4.1 Leaves mostly less than 20 cm long

a. Leaves narrow, 5-10 times longer than wide
- Trunk often crooked, low branches; small to medium-sized
    .... *Eucalyptus camaldulensis* 117
- Trunk straight, grey-white-bluish; medium to very large- sized;
twigs with waxy white coating .... *Eucalyptus grandis* 121

b. Leaves broader, less than 3 times longer than wide
- Buttresses
* Silvery/golden scales & hairs on leaf underside; fruit
large thorny, edible .... *Durio* 113
* Leaf stalk up to 8 cm long; fruit yellow-red, small, edible
    .... *Baccaurea ramiflora* 77
- No buttresses
* Leaf stalk 0.5-1 cm; flowers small, small trees; leaves aromatic smell
if crushed; flowers on stalks .... *Myristica* 163
* Leaf stalk 1 cm to very long;
- Leaves with prominent midrib below, parallel lateral
nerves, stalk up to 3.5 cm .... *Manilkara zapota* 155
- Leaf stalk up to 8 cm .... *Baccaurea ramiflora* 77

6.4.2 Leaves mostly more than 20 cm and up to 45 cm long

a. Leaf stalk 1-2.5 cm long
- Leaves narrow, green-grey, to 30 cm long
    .... *Eucalyptus camaldulensis* 117
- Leaves broader, shining, to 45 cm long .... *Bouea* 83

b. Leaf stalk 1.5-10 cm long
- Leaf stalk swollen at base .... *Mangifera indica* 151
- Leaf stalk not swollen at base .... *Mangifera altissima* 149

6.5.1 Very small to medium-sized trees; fleshy edible fruits

a. Fruits more than 10 cm long
- Leaves bad smell when crushed, fruit soft-spined
    .... *Annona muricata* 65
- Leaves pleasant smell, fruit pear-shaped .... *Persea americana* 171

b. Fruits less than 8 cm
- Leaves to 45 cm long; branchlets angular or flattened
    .... *Bouea* 83

- Leaves to 15 cm long, prominent midrib below
.... *Manilkara zapota* 155
- Leaves to 18 cm long, glandular .... *Baccaurea racemosa* 77

6.5.2 Medium to large-sized trees; fruits mostly small, not edible

a. Trunk often crooked; branchlets reddish; leaf stalk short
.... *Eucalyptus camaldulensis* 117
b. Straight trunk, bark white to grey-blue; leaf stalk short
.... *Eucalyptus grandis* 121

6.6 Leaves elliptic

6.6.1 Leaves 25-50 cm long

a. Branchlets and leaves hairy; sometimes buttresses
- Hairs on leaf midrib and veins below .... *Dimocarpus* 109
b. Branchlets and leaves without hairs; no buttresses
- Leaf stalk to 2.5 cm long; branchlets angular or flattened;
  flowers 4-merou .... *Bouea* 83
- Leaf stalk to 9 cm long; branchlets angular; flowers
  4-merous, white .... *Mangifera altissima* 149
- Leaf stalk to 8 cm, very swollen at base; flowers
  5-merous, reddish .... *Mangifera foetida* 149

6.6.2 Leaves 3-25 cm long

a. Twigs and/or leaves with hairs; edible fruits
- Both twigs and leaves with brown or reddish brown hairs
* Leaf stalk to 20 cm long; leaves hairy on midribs and veins only
  .... *Dimocarpus* 109
* Leaf stalk to 3 cm long .... *Artocarpus integer* 71
- Hairs on leaf underside only
* Large tree; leaves silvery or golden underneath .... *Durio* 113
* Shrub or small tree; leaves green .... *Annona squamosa* 65
b. Twigs and leaves without hairs
- Fruits edible fresh
* White latex in all parts; fruits very large, on stem and
  large branches .... *Artocarpus heterophyllus* 69
- Fruits drupes or berries, not edible fresh; Small tree
  leaves aromatic .... *Myristica* 163

SPECIES DESCRIPTIONS

Within each of the above groups the species desriptions are arranged alphabetically.

Notes to distribution maps:

Data on geographic distribution of tree species in Southeast Asia is still very limited and scattered. In most cases it has only been possible to determine if a particular species is present in a particular country or not, whereas its distribution within the country is not well known. In some countries, consisting of many islands, like Indonesia or the Philipines, it has been possible to specify the distribution of some species to certain islands. The relative abundance of each species is roughly indicated on the distribution maps by the following patterns;

Relative abundance:

High	Medium	Low	Non (or Rare)

Key characteristics: Tall straight-boled tree; grey and light brown pattern on trunk; rich in resin; leaves elliptical, 6-8 cm long with parallel nerves; seed cones roundish, about 8-10 cm in diameter.

CONIFERS and CASUARINAS

Agathis dammara
Araucariaceae

Synonyms: *Agathis loranthifolia, A. celebica, A. hamii*

Common names: dammar raja, kisi, salo (Ins); dayungon (Phi).

Description: A large tree up to 65 m tall and 200cm, or more, in diameter. Bark smooth, grey, coming off in large irregular plates producing a distinctive light brownish-grey pattern. Bark with abundant resin. Leaves smooth and shiny, oval to narrow elliptical, 6-8 cm long and 2-3 cm wide (smaller on fully exposed branches), tapering towards the rounded tip. Mature pollen cones up to 4-6 cm x 1.3 cm, on a stalk about 3 mm long. Mature seed cones oval to globular, 9-10.5 cm x 7.5-9.5 cm.

Use: Wood is used as general purpose softwood for boat building (masts), panelling, packaging, furniture, matches, household utensils, pencils, veneer, plywood, pulp and paper and many others. The tree is also an important source of a copal resin.

Ecology: It occurs scattered in lowland rain forests up to 1,200 m altitude, in the Philippines reported up to 2,100 m.

Disribution: Indonesia (Kalimantan and Sulawesi) and the Philippines.

References: Soerianegara & Lemmens (1994), Zamora et al. (1986).

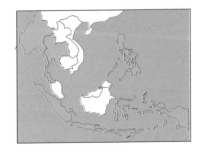

Key characteristics: Very tall, straight, evergreen tree; bark reddish-brown, brown to almost black, with wrinkles, fissures or ridges; branches in whorls; leaves lanceolate to triangular; seed cones to 10 cm long.

Trees and Fruits of Southeast Asia

Araucaria cunninghamii   Araucariaceae

Synonyms: *Araucaria beccarii*

Common names: Hoop pine, colonial pine, Richmond river pine (En); alloa, ningwik, pien (Ins); son naam (Tha).

Description: A very large evergreen, symmetrical tree with a tall straight cylindrical bole. Up to 60 (70) m tall and 200 cm in diameter. Bark reddish-brown or dark brown to almost black with transverse wrinkles, fissures or ridges. Branches often starting high on the bole, in whorls of 6-8, with leaf-bearing twigs all along their length. Leaves lanceolate to triangular with pointed apices slightly curved inward. Male (pollen) cones up to 8 cm long, mature female (seed) cones terminal, 6-10 x 5-8 cm with spiny winged scales. Seeds triangular, 20-30 mm x 9-10 mm, excluding wings.

Use: Yields excellent timber for all kinds of light construction and interior works, as well as for plywood and pulp that can be mixed with hardwood pulp. Seeds are edible.

Ecology: Most common above 1,000 m altitude where rainfall is high and temperatures range from 9-26°C. Pioneer species in disturbed habitats where soils may be very poor, leached, podzolic and acid. In Papua New Guinea it is commonly associated with species of Castanopsis, Cinnamomum, Podocarpus, Prumnopitys and Schizomeria.

Distribution: Native to Australia, Papua New Guinea and Indonesia and established as plantations in Burma, Thailand, Malaysia and the Philippines.

References: Soerianegara & Lemmens (1994).

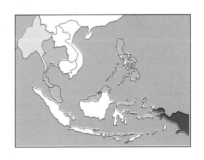

Key characteristics: Straight trunk; inner bark reddish, bitter or astringent; narrow, pointed feathery crown; pine like appearance; grey-green needles <30 cm long and 1 mm thick; cones small, 10-25 x 13-20 mm.

Casuarina Equisetifolia

Casuarinacae

Synonyms: *Casuarina litoralis, C. litorea*

Common names: Horse tail casuarina, casuarina, Australian pine (En); cemara laut (Ins); ru laut (Mal); tinyu (Bur); agoho (Phi); duong, phi-lao (Vie).

Description: A medium to large evergreen tree, 15-50 m tall and 20-100 cm in diameter. It looks like a pine tree at a di-stance. The trunk is very straight, first with smooth light grey-brown bark that later becomes thick, rough, furrowed and shaggy, splitting into strips and flakes exposing a reddish-brown inner layer. The crown is feathery, narrow and pointed. The "needles" are grey-green branchlets less than 30 cm long and 1 mm thick, with 5-8 branchlets per node and 7-8 cells per branchlet. The leaves are reduced to tiny scales at the nodes of the green branchlets. The male "flowers" in subterminal spikes formed of short, toothed cups (not illustrated). The fruit is a brown cone, oblong, 10-25 mm long and 13-20 mm wide, occurring in terminal heads (see illustration).

Use: Wood is used for fuelwood and charcoal, posts, poles, tool handles or made into pulp. Bark contains dye and also has medicinal use. Used for erosion control, dune stabilization, land reclamation and as windbreak.

Ecology: A pioneer species on sandy shores and river banks, very adaptable to a wide range of environmental conditions. It prefers alkaline to neutral soils, temperature between 10-35°C and rainfall between 700-2,000 mm but tolerates extremes outside these ranges well.

Distribution: Native to coastal areas from India to Polynesia and reported from Burma, Thailand, China, Vietnam, Malaysia, Indonesia and the Philippines.

References: Hensleigh & Holaway (1988), National Academy of Science (1980).

Key characteristics: Large; straight bole; deeply fissured bark; young twigs orange brown; needles in bundles of three (occasionally 2, 4 or 5), 15-25 cm long; cones single, 4-14 cm long.

Pinus caribaea
Pinaceae

Common names: Carribean pine, pitch pine, Nicaragua pine (En).

Description: A large tree up to 45 m high, but mostly smaller in plantations, with a straight cylindrical bole up to about 100 cm in diameter, deeply fissured bark and orange brown twigs later becoming grey-brown. Needles mostly in bundles of three, occasionally two, four or five, 15-25 cm long, in whorls at the end of shoots. Cones single, ovoid, 4-14 cm long. Divided into three varieties: var. hondurensis, the most common in Southeast Asia, var. caribaea and var. bahamensis.

Use: Wood is used for light construction, flooring, boxes and toys as well as for paper pulp, fibreboard and chipboard. Good quality oleoresin can be tapped from the stem.

Ecology: Growing naturally in a wide range of forest and savanna habitats as a pioneer species, for instance after fires, creating pure stands. Light demanding. In S.E. Asia grown only in strongly seasonal environments and light to medium textured neutral to acid soils. Tolerates seasonal waterlogging and salty winds.

Distribution: Native to Central America, now planted in many tropical areas including Burma, Thailand (trials), Malaysia, Indonesia and the Philippines.

References: Soerianegara & Lemmens (1994).

Key characteristics: Large; bark thick, reticulate, deeply fissured; branchlets often with white "powder"; needles 12-21 cm long, in bundles of 3 (sometimes 2 or 4); Cones up to 3 together, 5-8 cm long.

Pinus kesiya

Pinaceae

Synonyms: *Pinus insularis*, *P. khasya*

Common names: Benquet pine, khasya pine (En); khoua, mai hing (Lao); tinyu (Bur); son-sambai, chuang, kai-plueak-daeng (Tha); thoong ba las, xafnu (Vie).

Description: A large tree up to 45 m tall with first branches 15-20 m up, up to 100 cm in a trunk diameter. Bark thick, reticulate and deeply fissured. Branchlets often covered with white waxy "powder". Needles in bundles of 3 (occasionally 2 or 4), very slender and flexible, usually between 12 and 21 cm long, bright grass green. Cones up to 3 together, pendulous, ovoid to ovoid-conical, usually 5-8 cm long, stalkless or on stalk up to 10 mm long. The combination of P. khasya and P. insularis into one species - P. kesiya, is disputed by some botanists.

Use: General purpose timber as well as particle board and pulp. Oleoresin of good quality can be tapped from this species.

Ecology: Grows in areas with mean annual rainfall from 700 to 1,800 mm, a pronounced dry season and mean annual temperatures between 17-22°C. Pioneer species on a wide range of forest and savanna habitats following disturbances like fire. Very light demanding.

Distribution: Burma, Thailand, Laos, Cambodia, southern China, northern Vietnam and northern Philippines.

References: Soerianegara & Lemmens (1994).

Key characteristics: Large; straight bole; branches heavy, horizontal to ascending; bark thick, grey-brown, forming plates at base, reddish tinged higher up; needles in pairs, 16-25 cm long; cones single or in pairs, 5-11 cm long.

Pinus merkusii

Pinaceae

Synonyms: *Pinus sumatrana, P. merkusiana*

Common names: Merkus pine, Mondoro pine, Sumatran pine (En); damar batu, damar bunga, uyam (Ins); tapulau (Phi); son-song-bai, son-haang-maa, kai-plueak-dam (Tha); thoong nhuwja, thoong hai las (Vie).

Description: A large tree up to 70 m high and 55 cm trunk diameter on average (sometimes up to 150 cm) with straight, cylindrical bole free of branches up to 15-25 m in height. Branches are heavy and horizontal or ascending. Bark is thick, grey-brown and forming plates towards base, but scaly and reddish tinged higher up. Needles in pairs, slender, 16-25 cm long with persistent basal sheath. The cylindrical cones single or in pairs, 5-11 cm long. The seeds are small and have a 2.5 cm long wing.

Use: Used as a general purpose timber and for construction, boat building and flooring. A good quality oleoresin can be collected.

Ecology: The southernmost naturally occurring pine, growing up to 2,000 m altitude in areas with mean annual rainfall of 1,000-3,500 mm.

Distribution: From eastern Burma through northern Thailand to southern China, Indo-China, Indonesia and the Philippines.

References: Soerianegara & Lemmens (1994).

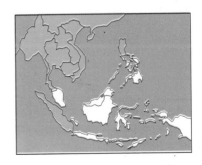

Dendrocalamus
asper

Dendrocalamus
giganteus

Bambusa vulgaris

Key characteristics: Woody, hollow culms with internodes; culms usually form clumps; thin branches from internodes; 8-18 leaves on each branchlet.

BAMBOOS
Bamboo spp. Gramineae

About 200 species of bamboo belonging to 20 genera are found in Southeast Asia, some of which are cultivated. The taxonomic classification is incomplete and unclear for several species. Here a general description is given with a few common species shown as examples.

Common names: Vernacular names for bamboo species are generally not very reliable and should be treated with caution as they can be misleading.

Description: Woody, usually hollow, erect, straight and smooth culms with internodes, some species up to 30 m tall and 25 cm in culm diameter. In most genera the culms form clumps at base. Average length between internodes is 35 cm but may be more than one metre in some species. Climbing species also exist. Branches and culm sheaths arise from internodes. The culm sheets, which usually falls off when the culm matures, often have irritant hairs on the outside. Each branchlets bears 8-18 leaves. Most species with lance shaped, thin leaves with parallel venation pattern and a leaf stalk. New culm shoots are produced every year from the rhizomes (underground stems).

Use: Countless uses in light construction, furniture making, basket weaving, for musical instruments and handicrafts, as containers or as raw material for paper production or bamboo plywood. Young shoots of many species, including *Dendrocalamus asper* are edible.

Ecology: Most bamboos flowers only rarely, at intervals varying from 20 to 120 years, after which the plant dies. In some species the whole population flowers simultaneously, in others the flowering is individual but some, like the genus Schizostachyum flower continuously and do not die afterwards.

Distribution: Distributed all over Southeast Asia.

References: Dransfield & Widjaja (1995).

Key characteristics: Slender erect palm; young stem green, later greyish brown; 8-12 leaves, 1-1.5 m long; single branched inflorescence from stem under crown; fruits yellow to orange.

PALM and BANANAS

Areca catechu

Palmae

Synonyms: Also spelled *Areca cathecu*

Common names: Betel palm, areca palm (En); pinang, pinang siri (Mal); kunthi-pin kun (Bur); bunga (phi); maak mia (Tha); cao (Vie).

Description: A slender, erect, palm up to 30 m tall and 25-40 cm in diameter. Stem straight, green when young, later becoming greyish brown, with rings from leaf scars. 8-12 leaves, 1-1.5 m long, even pinnate, with 30-50 leaflets, each 30-70 cm long and 3-7 cm wide are forming the crown, about 2.5 m in diameter. A single, branched inflorescence from the stem under the crown. Male flowers numerous, small, borne above female flowers, 3-merous. Female flowers on thickened base of branches, 1.2-2 cm long, green and creamy-white. Fruits 5-10 x 3-5 cm, variable in shape, yellow to orange when ripe, 50-400 fruits on one stand.

Use: The hard, dried endosperm of ripe and unripe seeds (the "nuts") are chewed as a narcotic, sometimes alone, but usually mixed with the leaves of betel-pepper (Piper betel) and slaked lime.

Ecology: Grows from sea level to about 900 m altitude, particular in coastal climates, where evenly distributed annual rainfall of 1,500-5,000mm ensures ample soil moisture throughout the year.

Distribution: Origin unclear, but probably in north eastern Indonesia. In Southeast Asia, it is found in Burma, Thailand, Vietnam, Malaysia, Indonesia and the Philippines.

References: Purseglove (1985), Whitmore (1979).

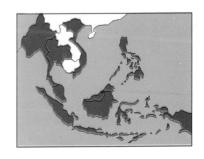

Key characteristics: Very dense, relatively small crown;
leaves fan-shaped with short thick stalks; smooth stem; fruits
to 20 cm in diameter, yellowish.

Borassus flabellifer
Palmae

Common names: Palmyra palm (En); lontar (Mal); htan, htan-taw (Bur); taan (Tha); thót-lót (Vie).

Description: Solitary fan palm up to 20 m tall with stiffly projecting leaves and very dense, blue-green crown. Stem smooth. Leaf stalks short, massive and yellowish, finely toothed on margins (but appearing smooth from a distance). Leaf blade fan-shaped, 1-1.3 m across. Inflorescence about 1 m long, hanging down through split leaf base. Fruits roundish, 15-20 cm in diameter, yellow when ripe. Similar species: May occasionally be confused with two other genuses of fan palms *Corypha* and *Livistonia*. However, *Corypha* has much larger leaves with massive spines and only flowers once, producing a huge tree-like inflorescence, after which it dies. *Livistonia* also have much larger spines on the leaf stalks than *Borassus* but the stalks themselves are more slender, resulting in a more open crown. Fruits of *Livistonia* are much smaller than *Borassus*, ranging from 1.5-7.5 cm in diameter.

Use: Sugar and toddy is produced from sap extracted from young inflorescence. Young fruits edible and their juice used for flavouring cakes. Fibres can be extracted from the base of the leaf stalks.

Ecology: According to Purseglove (1985), it does not thrive in extremely humid climates, although it is often found along water courses in drier areas.

Distribution: From Africa through Madagascar, India and Sri Lanka to Burma, Thailand, Indo-China, Malaysia, Indonesia, and further east.

References: Purseglove (1985), Whitmore (1979).

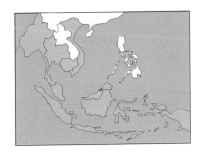

Key characteristics: Feather shaped leaves; leaf scars on stem, character-istic big, green-yellowish to brown fruits - usually year round. Naturalized in coastal areas.

Cocos nucifera
Palmae

Common names: Coconut palm (En); kelapa (Ins, Mal); on, mak-un (Bur); niog (Phi); ma-praaw (Tha); dùa (Vie).

Description: It grows to 25 m in height. The trunk is 20-40 cm in diameter at breast height and marked with leaf scars. Leaves on adult trees are 4-5.5 m long with a stalk of 1 m or longer. The more than 100 pairs of leaflets are linear to lanceolate, acuminate and up to 1 m long. Inflorescence is about 1 m long or less with female flowers at the base of the stalk and male near the terminal end. Fruits are round, sometimes 3-angled, 15-25 cm long and covered with a thick fibrous husk. Many different types of coconut palms exist, including dwarf types.

Use: Literally hundreds of uses have been recorded. These include timber, posts, fencing, food, fuel, drinks, thatching, basket making, mats, brushes, brooms, utensils, alcohol and oils.

Ecology: The coconut palm prefers warm lowland habitats with evenly distributed rainfall of 1,500 mm or more annually. Although often regarded as a coastal plant, it can be found far inland and at elevations up to 1,500 m. The fruit tolerates long periods in salt water which has probably contributed to the very wide distribution of this species.

Distribution: The origin of this palm is not known, already prehistorically it was distributed throughout the tropics and is now naturalized on tropical shores worldwide, including all countries of Southeast Asia.

References: F/FRED (1992), Guzman & Fernando (1986), Hensleigh & Holaway (1988), Purseglove (1978), Westphal & Jansen (1993), Whitmore (1979).

Key characteristics: Unbranched palm; leaf bases remain on stem at least 12 years; leaves up to 7.5 m long, with spiny leaf stalk.

Elaeis guineensis   Palmae

Common names: Oil palm (En); dôong preeng (Cam); kelapa sawit, salak minyak (Ins); kelapa bali, kelapa sawit (Mal); si-ohn, si-htan (Bur); pan namman (Tha); co dâù, dùa dâù (Vie).

Description: Unbranched erect tree up to 20-30 m tall and 22-75 cm in diameter. The crown has about 40-60 live dark green leaves and a skirt of dead leaves (less leaves if trimmed as is common in plantations). Each leaf up to 7.5 m long with 60-160 pairs of leaflets and spiny leaf stalk. Leaf bases remain on a stem for at least 12 years giving a rough-stemmed palm. Later, when fallen off, the stem becomes smooth. The inflorescence is produced from about every second leaf axil. There are up to 1,500 deep violet fruits (ripening to orange-red) in each roundish dense cluster, weighing 30 kg or more. Individual fruits are about 4 cm long, oval, broadly triangular and with the style remaining on the tip.

Use: Mainly grown for its high production of palm oil and palm kernel oil used for making margarine, cooking oil and other food products and soaps and detergents. The press cake remaining after extracting the oil is an important livestock food. Palm wine can be made from sap tapped from the male inflorescence and the central shoot is edible. Leaves are used for roof-thatching.

Ecology: Its natural habitat is considered to be along tropical rain forest water courses or in freshwater swamps or in other disturbed forest habitats where adequate light is available. It prefers 2,000 mm of annual rain or more and warm tropical temperatures and grows on a wide range of soils.

Distribution: Originates in West Africa but is now widely grown in many tropical countries including Thailand, China, Malaysia, Indonesia and the Philippines.

References: Guzman & Fernando (1986), Purseglove (1985), Whitmore (1979).

Musa spp.
(edible type)

Musa textilis

Musa spp.
Key characteristics: Branchless herb; green stem; leaves to 4 m long from center of stem; Single, large inflorescence through center of pseudo-stem; many varieties.

Musa textilis
Key characteristics: Slender; leaves smaller, reddish when young; fruits with seeds.

Musa spp. Edible forms — Musaceae

Common names: Banana (En); cheek nam' vaa (Cam); pisang (Ins, Mal); kwàyz (Lao); nget pyo thee (Bur); gluay (Tha); chuôí (Vie).

Description: Tree-like perennial herb, 2-9 m tall. Tightly rolled over-lapping leaf sheath forms a cylindrical pseudo-stem, 20-50 cm in diameter. New leaves grow up through the centre of the pseudo-stem. The leaf blade is 1.5-4m long and 0.7-1m wide with pronounced supporting midrib. A single terminal inflorescence appear through centre of pseudo-stem, bending down when exerted, male flowers towards tip of stand, female behind these. Flower/fruit stand 50-150 cm long when mature. Fruits berrylike, seedless, curved 6-35 cm long, 2.5-5 cm wide, green, yellow or reddish.

Use: Grown primarily for the fruit which, depending on cultivar can be eaten fresh, cooked or preserved in various ways. The male bud is eaten as a vegetable. Leaves are used for packing, wrapping and decorative purposes.

Ecology: Although banana has a wide temperature tolerance, growth and production are far better in warm tropical climates. It requires steady moisture supply of about 200 mm a month and plenty of sunlight. It prefers neutral to acid, deep, friable loams with high organic matter content.

Distribution: Exact origin unknown, but now all over the tropics and subtropics.

Musa textilis

Common names: Manila hemp

Description: Structure similar to the edible bananas but more slender with smaller leaves and seeded fruits. Leaves reddish when mature.

Use: The very strong and resilient fibres from the outer sheets of the leaf stalks are used for producing ropes, fishing nets, hammocks, hats and mats. Lower grades are used for special types of paper production.

Ecology: Like the edible bananas

Distribution: Philippines, Malaysia and Indonesia.

References: Purseglove (1985), Verheij & Coronel (1992), Westphal & Jansen (1993).

Key characteristics: Very thorny climbing palms with slender and flexible stems; mostly unbranched; thorny whip-like climbing organs.

Rattans   Araceae (or Palmae)

Almost 600 species of climbing palms of which nearly 400 belongs to the genera *Calamus*. Other major genera represented in southeast Asia are: *Daemonorops* (115 species), *Korthalsia* (26) and *Plectocomia* (16).

Common names: Rattan, canes (En); rotan (Ins,Mal); kyin (Bur); wai (Tha).

Description: Spiny, climbing (except a few species) palms with solid but very long and flexible, mostly cylindrical stems. Some are single-stemmed, some multi-stemmed, with stem diameters ranging from a few mm to more than 10 cm. Leaves with or without stalk, usually armed with spines in species characteristic arrangements, in some species extending into long spiny whip-like climbing organ (cirrus). Other species (many *Calamus*) have similar organ (flagellum) arising from the leaf sheath on the stem. Single inflorescence is produced at the node (stem-section), borne in the leaf axil. Most genera have male and female flowers on separate plants. *Korthalsia* has, however, hermaphroditic flowers.

Use: The stems are extensively used for making cane furniture, mats, baskets and rope. Young shoots and fruits of some species are edible.

Ecology: Varies between species due and the wide geographical range. Rattan species are found in most forest types and on most soil and rock types, from sea level to 3,000 m altitude. Different species are adapted to a range of light conditions.

Distribution: From equatorial Africa, through Indian subcontinent, Sri Lanka, southern China, the Malay Archipelago to Australia and the western Pacific including Fiji. The greatest number of genera and species are found in western Malesia*.

References: Dransfield & Manokaran (1994).

* Malesia is the bio-geographical region including Malaysia, Indonesia, Singapore,Brunei, the Philippines and Papua New Guinea.

Key characteristics: Small to medium sized; crooked stem; richly branched. "Leaves" are flattened leaf stalks with parallel nervation; small yellow flowers and coiled seed pods.

BROADLEAVED TREES

Acacia auriculiformis
Leguminosae (Mimosoideae)

Synonyms: *Acacia moniliformis, A. auriculaeformis*

Common names: Japanese acacia, tan wattle, northern black wattle, earpod wattle, Darwin black wattle (Aus), kasia (Ins), auri (Phi).

Description: A small to medium sized fast-growing tree, 8-25 m high, diameter reaching 60 cm. Often with crooked (and multiple) stem and low and heavy branch-ing. Bark grey or brown, first smooth, then becoming rough and fissured. Flattened leaf stalks acting as leaves (phyllodes) are 10-18 cm long and 2-3 cm wide with parallel veins. Seedlings with small compound leaves. Minute yellow flowers in up to 8 cm long spikes. Fruits are 6-8 cm long coiled pods with brown seeds attached by orange filaments. Hybridizes with *A. mangium*.

Use: Erosion control, land reclamation and soil improvement. The wood is used for pulp, fuelwood and has limited use for construction, implements and furniture. The bark contains tannins.

Ecology: In its native habitat a colonizer of tropical coastal lowlands and found along streams, in open forests, savannas and adjacent to mangroves, often in sandy soils. Very tolerant to different soil conditions and water supply. Thrives best in seasonal climates receiving 2,000-2,500 mm annual rainfall but may here become quite competitive towards other species.

Distribution: Native to Papua New Guinea, islands in the Torres Straits and northern Australia, but has been introduced to Burma, Thailand, Malaysia, Indonesia and the Philippines.

References: Awang & Taylor (1993), Hensleigh & Holaway (1988), Little (undated), MacDicken (1994), National Research Council (1980).

Key characteristics: Small tree; sharp thorns; bark red on back; bipinnate leaves, 9-17 cm long, numerous small stalkless leaflets; 5-merous yellow or pale yellow flowers.

Acacia catechu

Leguminosae (Mimosoideae)

Synonyms: *Acacia catechuoides, A. polyacantha, A. wallichiana, Mimosa catechu, M. catechuoides*

Common names: Cutch (En); Tun-sa-se, Nya, Shaji, Mung-ting (Bur); seesiat (Tha)

Description: A small deciduous or semi-deciduous tree that grows up to 10-15 m tall and 50 cm in diameter. Bark dark, greyish and rough, 1cm thick, red on the inside. Thorns on the trunk and branches. Leaves are bipinnate, 9-17 cm long with numerous small, stalkless leaflets. The small yellow or pale yellow 5-merous flowers are arranged in 5-10 cm long, cylindrical spikes arising from leaf corners (axils). The fruit is a long, straight, dark-brown flat pod, 5-10 cm long, smooth and pointed at both ends.

Use: The heartwood is used for the manufacturing of *katha*, an important ingredient in traditional chewing mixture (e.g. in Burma) and cutch which is used for tanning, dyeing and as viscosity adjuster in oil drilling. The wood is generally used as fuelwood and bark as well as seeds have medicinal properties.

Ecology: Grows in open, drier areas mostly on well drained soil types, but can also be found on shallow, poor, rocky soils. In Thailand found in mixed deciduous forest.

Distribution: Occurs naturally in India, Burma and Thailand.

References: FAO (1992).

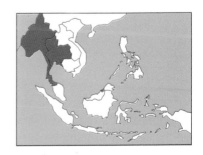

Key characteristics: Straight bole with rough bark. "Leaves" are actually flattened leaf stalks with characteristic parallel veins; flowers creamy-white; seed pods becomes twisted.

Acacia mangium
Leguminosae (Mimosoideae)

Synonyms: *Acacia glaucescens, Mangium montanum.*

Common names: Brown salwood, mangium, black wattle, hickory wattle (En), maber (Phi).

Description: Mature trees up to 30 m tall and 25-50 cm in diameter (-90 cm). Often straight bole unbranched to about half height. Bark is pale grey-brown to brown, rough and furrowed. The young leaves are compound, but are replaced after a few weeks by flattened petioles (phyllodes), up to 25 cm long and 5-10 cm wide. Flowers are white or creamy white and arranged in loose spikes. Seed pods are initially straight but twists into spiralled clusters. *A. mangium* may hybridize with *A. auriculiformis* where these occur together. Hybrids show intermediate growth patterns but usually have lighter coloured bark than the parent species.

Use: Soil enrichment in agroforestry systems. Wood for timber, pulp, particle board, furniture and fuelwood. The "leaves" can be given to livestock as emergency food.

Ecology: In native habitats it is usually found at elevations below 300 m, but may occur up to 700 m and where annual rainfall is from 1,000 to 4,500 mm. Although it survives long dry seasons, growth is greatly reduced.

Distribution: Originates in northeastern Australia, Papua New Guinea and Indonesia but is now widely planted in many countries, including Thailand, Malaysia, Indonesia and the Philippines.

References: Awang & Taylor (1993), F/FRED (1992), Hensleigh & Holaway (1988), MacDicken (1994).

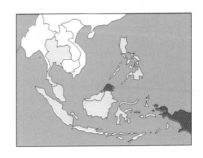

Key characteristics: Small; deciduous; spines on branches;
trunk base usually fluted; bark grey, cracking vertically into
scales; leaves alternate, tri-foliate; flowers greenish-white;
fruits with woody shell.

Aegle marmelos

Rutaceae

Common names: Bael (En); bnau (Cam); maja, maja batuh (Ins); toum (Lao): bilak, bila, bel (Mal); opesheet, ohshit (Bur); matum, tum, ma pin (Tha); trái mam (Vie).

Description: A small, deciduous tree up to 15 m high and 50 cm in diameter with 1-2 cm long spines on older branches. Trunk usually fluted at base. The bark is grey and rather corky and cracks vertically into long scales. Leaves alternate, trifoliate, on 2-4 cm long stalk. The two lower leaflets are ovate to elliptic, up to 7 cm long and 4 cm wide. The terminal leaflet is obovate and slightly larger (7.5 x 4.8 cm). The inflorescence is a 4-5 cm long raceme from the leaf corner with greenish-white flowers, about 2 cm in diameter. Fruits smooth, irregular roundish, grey or yellowish, 5-12.5 cm in diameter, often with hard woody shell and 6-10 seeds in clear, sticky pulp.

Use: Fruits are eaten fresh or prepared as sherbet, syrup or marmalade. From the fruit household glue, dye, tanning agent and various medicines can be produced. Bark, leaves and roots have a number of medicinal uses and the bark can also be used as fish poison. The wood can be used for making small articles such as handles. The tree is very sacred in Hindu religion.

Ecology: Hardy subtropical species tolerating temperature extremes from -7 to 49°C and growing on swampy as well as dry soils. Only flowers and fruits well where there is a prominent dry season.

Distribution: From the Indian peninsula, bael has spread to Burma, Thailand, Vietnam, Malaysia, Indonesia and the Philippines.

References: Storrs (1990), Verheij & Coronel (1992).

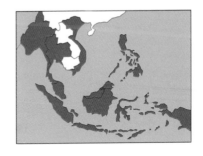

Key characteristics: Large spreading crown; smooth grey bark becoming rough and fissured by age; inner bark pink; leaves even bipinnate, leaflets 2-5 cm, flower heads puffball-like, 3-4 cm in diameter, white; pods yellow, 10-25 cm long, flat.

Albizia lebbeck

Leguminosae
(Mimosoideae)

Synonyms: *Mimosa lebbeck*, *M. sirissa*, *Acacia lebbeck*. (also spelled lebbek)

Common names: Kokko (Bur); langil (Phi); kasuek, kampu, kasae, hop-hoan (Tha).

Description: A medium sized tree up to 30 m tall and 1 m in diameter (occasionally up to 3 m), with a large spreading crown and smooth grey bark, becoming fissured and rough by age; inner bark pink and bitter tasting. Leaves alternate, evenly bipinnate, 15-40 cm long, with a gland at the base on the upper side of the axes, 2-4 pairs of lateral axes, each with 4-12 pairs of leaflets. Leaflets 2-5 cm long and 1-2.5 cm wide, oblong and broadly rounded or emarginate. The puffball-like flower heads are 3-4 cm in diameter, with many tiny white flowers with greenish yellow corolla and borne on 6 cm long stalks. Fruit pods golden yellow, leathery, 10-25 cm long and 2.5-4 cm wide when mature, flat, but swollen around the seeds.

Use: Wood is used for fuel, carving, construction and furniture. Young leaves can be used as livestock feed or green fertilizer. Exudes a valuable gum. Bark is used for soap production and honey can be produced from the nectar.

Ecology: In its native habitat it grows in savanna areas and tolerates a wide range of soils except very eroded sites, but prefers moist well drained loams, neutral to slightly acidic. Fixes nitrogen.

Distribution: Originates in Pakistan, India, Bangladesh, Nepal and Burma and now also cultivated in Thailand, Cambodia, Malaysia, Vietnam and the Philippines.

References: Guzman et al (1986), Hensleigh & Holaway (1988), Mac-Dicken (1994), Smitinand & Larsen (1985).

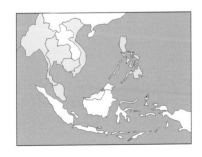

Key characteristics: Often large, with very wide, low crown; brown-black fissured bark; bipinnate leaves, leaflets 1.5-4 cm long, wider towards tip; crimson to pink flowers, pods 12-25 cm long, 2 cm wide.

Albizia saman

Leguminosae
(Mimosoideae)

Synonyms: *Samanea saman, Pithecellobium saman, Enterolobium saman, Mimosa saman, Inga saman, Inga salutaris*

Common names: Raintree, monkey pod, saman, french tamarind (En); acacia (Phi); kam kram, cham cha (Tha); còng (Vie).

Description: A large tree up to 45 (60) m high and 2 m in diameter, with a very wide and low crown up to 55-60 m wide. The bark is brown to black, developing ridges with age. Leaves are evenly bipinnate, up to 15-30 cm long with 8-12 pinnae. Leaflets are 1.5-6 cm long and 0.7-4 cm wide, blunt at base and tip, with a minute point at the tip and a short point at the base. Leaflets are larger at apical end of pinnae than at base and number 12-16 in outer pinnae and 6-10 in lower. Flowers are numerous, pink, alone or in sub-globose heads from the leaf corners, 5-7 cm in diameter. Pods with fleshy pulp, 12-25 cm long and 2 cm wide with sweet, brown pulp.

Use: Mostly used as ornamental shade tree or shade tree on pasture land. Wood is used for carving and furniture, construction, boats, veneer and plywood. Fair fuelwood quality. Leaves can be used as forage and the pods are edible. The tree also contains gum and resin.

Ecology: Grows in tropical areas with mean annual temperatures of about 22°C at altitudes from sea level to 700 m, where annual rainfall ranges from 600 to 2,500 mm and the dry season is less than 6 months. Light demanding but tolerates a wide range of soil types.

Distribution: From the West Indies it has been introduced throughout the tropics and have naturalized in many areas, including all the countries covered by this guide.

References: Hensleigh & Holaway (1988).

Key characteristics: Medium to large sized; cylindrical bole; large buttresses when older; outer bark coming off in small papery flakes; leaves in whorls of 5-8; fruits 20-40 cm long, slender follicles.

Alstonia scholaris   Apocynaceae

Synonyms: *Echites scolaris, E. pala, Tabernaemontana alternifolia*

Common names: White cheesewood, milkwood pine, blackboard tree (En); pulai lilin (Bru); pulai, pule, rite (Ins); tinpet (Lao); pulai (Mal); lettok (Bur); dita, dalipoen (Phi); sattaban, teenpethasaban (Tha); caay mof cua, caay suwxa (Vie).

Description: A medium to large tree up to 40 m high and 125 cm in diameter with a cylindrical bole. Older trees with buttresses up to 6 m high and reaching 2 m out from a bole. Outer bark brown or yellowish white, smooth, coming off in small papery flakes; inner bark yellow to brown with white latex. Leaves 7-23 cm long, in whorls of 4-8 on 1.5-3 cm long petiole, oblong-lanceolate or elliptical with rounded tip and numerous secondary veins. Flowers greenish to yellow, fragrant, with soft haired calyx. The fruits are slender cylindrical follicles, 20-40 cm long and 4-5 mm in diameter.

Use: Most important source of pulai timber. Wood yields good pulp. Bark and latex is used medicinally for many purposes.

Ecology: Most abundant in monsoon areas. Tolerates a variety of soils and habitats and found up to 500 m, sometimes even to 1,000 m altitude.

Distribution: Widely distributed from Sri Lanka and India through mainland Southeast Asia, southern China, Malaysia, Indonesia and the Philippines to Australia, and also planted elsewhere.

References: Guzman et al (1986), Soerianegara & Lemmens (1994).

Key characteristics: Small tree, wide dome-shaped crown, low crooked branches, smooth brown bark, large simple obovate, dark green shining leaves with prominent midribs and veins, very characteristic fruit.

Anacardium occidentale   Anacardiaceae

Synonyms: *Cassurium reniforme*

Common names: Cashew (En); svaay chantii (Cam); jambu monyet, jambu mede (Ins); Gajus, jambu monyet (Mal); thiho thayet si (Bur); kasoy, balubad, balogo (Phi); mamuang himmaphan, yaruang, mamuang letlor (Tha); dào lôn hôt, cay diêù (Vie).

Description: An evergreen tree up to 12 m high with a dome-shaped crown. Branching starts at 0.5-1.5 m above the ground. Bark is smooth and brown. Leaves alternate, on 1-2 cm long stalks, obovate to obovate-oblong, up to 20 x 15 cm, leathery, red-brown when young, later shining green, smooth, with prominent midrib and veins. Flower stands terminal, drooping panicles, up to 25 cm long with fragrant flowers with 5 petals, 7-13 mm long and 5 sepals, 4-15 mm long. Male flowers with 7-9 stamens, hermaphroditic flowers usually with 9 short and 1 long viable stamen. First whitish later turning pinkish-red. The "real" fruit is a kidney shaped nut about 3 x 1.2 cm sitting on the much enlarged and swollen flower stalk - the fruit-like cashew apple, which is pear shaped, 10-20 cm x 4-8 cm and red to yellow.

Use: Nuts are used as a main food or delicacy depending on availability. The cashew apple is eaten fresh, mixed in fruit salads or made into juice. Seed coats and shells are used as poultry feed. Valuable oil can be extracted from the shell. The wood is used as fuel or low quality timber. Cashew also contains tannins and gum. Young shoots and leaves are eaten raw or cooked. All tree parts are used in traditional medicine, especially for treating skin ailments.

Ecology: Requires high temperatures. Rainfall distribution more important than amount. Tolerates dry conditions if roots have access to soil moisture.

Distribution: From its native Brazil introduced throughout most of the tropics. In this region reported from all countries except Laos.

References: Hensleigh & Holaway (1988), Verheij & Coronel (1992).

Annona
muricata

Annona
squamosa

A. muricata
Key characteristics: Leaves
bad smelling when crushed;
flowers large yellow-green,
strong smell; fruit with soft
spines.

A. squamosa
Key characteristics: Leaves
hairy; petals green; fruit
green-ish yellow, powdery
surface, 5-10 cm in diameter.

Annona muricata
Annonaceae

Common names: Guayabano, soursop (En); tiep barang (Cam); sirsak, nangka belanda (Ins); khan thalot, khièp thét (Lao); durian belanda (Mal); duyin-awza (Bur); guayabano (Phi); thurian thet, rian nam (Tha); mang câu xiêm (Vie).

Description: 5 to 9 m high tree, branching from near base. Leaves alternate, short stalked, oblong ovate, entire, 7-20cm long and 2-5cm wide, pointed in both ends, dark green and shiny above, yellowish green below, badly smelling when crushed. Flowers large, yellowish green, strong smelling, 1 or 2 together. Flower stalk with short dense hairs. Fruit tender with leathery skin and soft, curved spines. Flesh whitish, very juicy with hard, dark brown seeds.

Use: Immature fruits eaten as vegetable, mature fruits fresh or made into juice, preserve, jam or jelly. Leaves and roots used for traditional medicinal purposes.

Ecology: Grows in tropical climates below 1,000 m altitude with minimum 1,000 mm annual rain, but tolerates up to 6 month drought. Cannot tolerate water-logging and needs well drained not too acid soil.

Distribution: From tropical America it is now widely distributed in lowland tropics.

Annona squamosa
Annonaceae

Common names: Sugar apple, sweetsop (En); tiep baay, tiep srok (Cam); Sirkaja, sarikaja, atis (Ins), khieb (Lao); nona sri kaya, buah nona, sri kaya (Mal), awza (Bur); atis (Phi); noina, makkhiap, lanang (Tha); na, mang câu ta (Vie).

Description: Shrub or small tree, 3-6m high. Leaves oblong to narrowly elliptic, 7-17cm long and 3-5.5cm wide, slightly hairy or smooth beneath. Flowers in groups of 2-4 or sometimes alone, on slender stalks on young branchlets. Outer 3 petals oblong to 2.5cm long, green with purple base whereas inner 3 petals are reduced or absent. Fruit globose, 5-10cm in diameter, greenish-yellow with powdery surface. Commercial hybrids with *A. cherimola* called atemoya or custard apple.

Use: As fresh fruit or flavoring.

Ecology: Like *A. muricata*.

Distribution: As *A. muricata*. Grown commercially in Thailand, Malaysia and the Philippines.

References: Hensleigh & Holaway (1988), Purseglove (1968), Verheij & Coronel (1991).

Key characteristics: Medium sized; often buttresses; twigs very thick; leaves large, lobed, leathery dark green; male inflorescence club-shaped, yellowish, female stands round, green; fruit large, round, yellow green; all parts with white latex.

Artocarpus altilis   Moraceae

Synonyms: *Artocarpus communis, A. camansi*

Common names: Breadfruit (En); sakéé, khnaôr samloo (Cam); sukun (seedless), kelur, timbul (seeded) (Ins, Mal); paung-thi (Bur); rimas (seedless), kamansii (seeded) (Phi); sake (seedless), khanun-sampalor (Tha); sakê (Vie).

Description: An evergreen or semi-deciduous tree, up to 30 m tall and 1.8 m in diameter, often buttressed. Twigs very thick. Leaves alternate, ovate to elliptical in form, 20-60 cm x 20-40 cm, first undivided, later deeply pinnately cut into 5-11 lobes, thick, leathery, dark green and shiny above, pale green and rough below. Leaf stalk 3-5 cm long. Male and female inflorescences separate, but on same tree, axillary on 4-8 cm long flower stalks. Male stands drooping, club-shaped, 15-25 cm long and 3-4 cm wide, spongy and yellow. Female stands upright, globose or cylindrical, 8-10 cm x 5-7 cm with numerous green flowers embedded in receptacle. The fruit is formed from the entire female inflorescence, cylindrical to globose, 10-30 cm in diameter, yellow-green, sometimes with short spines. All tree parts with white latex.

Use: Immature and ripe fruit and seeds are eaten after boiling, baking, roasting or frying. Leaves and fallen fruit are good animal feed. Wood used for light construction, canoes and others. Different plant parts have various medicinal uses. Sometimes used as wind-break or shade tree for coffee.

Ecology: Wet tropic species, preferring 20-40°C, 2,000-3,000 mm annual rainfall, moist, deep, humus rich and well drained soils at altitudes below 600 m.

Distribution: Origin uncertain, now widely distributed throughout tropics, including all countries covered by this field guide.

References: Verheij & Coronel (1992).

Key characteristics: Flowers and fruits from stem and major branches (cauliflory). Fruits very large, weighing from 10-50 kg. All living parts exude viscid, white latex when injured.

Artocarpus heterophyllus   Moraceae

Synonyms: *Artocarpus philippensis, A. brasiliensis, A. maxima*

Common names: Jackfruit (En); khnaor (Cam); nangka (Ins,Mal); miiz, miiz hnang (Lao); peignai (Bur); langka (Phi); khanon, makmi, banun (Tha); mit (Vie).

Description: A medium size, evergreen tree reaching 20 (-30) m in height and 80 (-200) cm in diameter. Bark rough to scaly, dark grey to greyish-brown. Leaves of young plants with 1-2 pair of lobes, whereas older leaves with entire margin (hence "heterophyllus"), obovate-elliptic to elliptic, thin leathery, 5-25 x 3-12 cm, broadest at the middle. Similar species: *A. altilis* fruits are smaller and more round, hanging from tip of branches. Leaves are much larger and deeply cut (see preceding page). *A. integer* has hairy leaves and twigs and the fruits are much smaller (next page).

Use: Young fruit as vegetable, ripe fruit eaten fresh or made in to various sweet dishes. Seeds eaten after boiling, roasting or drying. Young leaves used as livestock fodder. Tannin from bark. Dyes from wood particles. Latex used as glue and cement. Timber medium hardwood, termite resistant. Renowned for a number of medical properties.

Ecology: Originates from evergreen forest at 400-1,200 m altitude. Prefers annual rainfall above 1,500 mm and well drained alluvial, sandy or clay loam soils with pH 6-7.5.

Distribution: Probably originates in Western Ghats, India, but has been introduced throughout the tropics, particularly Southeast Asia.

References: Hensleigh & Holaway (1988), Purseglove (1968), Verheij & Coronel (1991).

Key characteristics: Rarely buttresses; bark grey-brown, bumpy; twigs and leaves with brown hair; leaves obovate to elliptic; fruit cylindrical to round, yellowish to brownish to orange-green.

Artocarpus integer   Moraceae

Synonyms: *Artocapus integrifolia, A. polyphema, A. champeden*

Common names: Cempedak (En); chempedak, campedak, baroh (Ins); chempedak [cultivated], bankong [wild] (Mal); sonekadat (Bur); champada (Tha); mit tó nù (Vie).

Description: An evergreen tree up to 20 m high, rarely with buttresses. Bark grey-brown and bumpy. Twigs and leaves with brown hairs. Leaves obovate to elliptic, 5-25 cm long and 2.5-12 cm wide with cuneate to rounded base, entire margin, pointed tip and 6-10 pairs of lateral veins curving forward. The leaf stalk is 1-3 cm long. Fruit cylindrical to almost globose, 20-35cm x 10-15cm, yellowish to brownish to orange-green.

Use: The fruit flesh surrounding the seeds are eaten fresh or cooked. The seeds can be eaten after roasting or boiling. Young fruits and sometimes young leaves can be cooked and eaten as a vegetable. The strong and durable wood are used for building construction, furniture and boats. The bark can be used for rope making and the latex for making lime.

Ecology: Understorey tree commonly growing in secondary and sometimes in primary forests in lowland tropical rainforest areas up to 500 m altitude or sometimes higher, where there is no distinct dry season. Prefers well drained soils but tolerates temporary water-logging.

Distribution: Burma, Thailand, Vietnam, Malaysia and Indonesia.

References: Verheij & Coronel (1992).

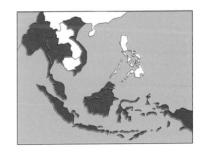

Averrhoa
bilimbi

Averrhoa
carambola

A. bilimbi
Key characteristics: Small
tree; upright branches, pinnate leaves, 7-19 pairs of
ovate leaflets +one terminal
leaflet; some of the flowers on
stem (cauliflower); fruit yellow-green, slightly lobed.

A. carambola
Key characteristics: Bushy
tree; drooping branches, 3-6
pairs of leaflets, purple-red
flowers; shiny yellow fruit with
5 pronounced ribs.

Averrhoa bilimbi Oxalidaceae

Common names: Billimbi, cucumber tree (En); tralong tong (Cam); belimbing asam, belimbing wuluh, belimbing buluk (Ins, Mal); tayok-zaungya (Bur); kamias, iba (Phi); taling pling (Tha); khe tau (Vie).

Description: A small tree with few, upright, branches, 6-9 m high. Leaves pinnate usually with 7-19 pairs of 5-12 cm long ovate leaflets and a single terminal leaflet. Flowers auxiliary or cauliflorous, with 10-22 mm long, red-purple coloured, free petals. Fruit a yellowish-green berry, slightly lobed and up to 10 x 5 cm.

Use: Fruit used for pickles, curries, chutney and preserves in syrup and can also be used to clean metal and remove stains. Also used in traditional medicines.

Ecology: Prefer seasonal humid climates with a drier season, but not actual drought and slightly acid soils. Flooding and salinity is not tolerated.

Distribution: Origin S.E. Asia, now grown all over the humid tropics.

Averrhoa carambola Oxalidaceae

Common names: Carambola, star fruit (En); spo (Cam); fuand (Lao); belimbing manis (Mal, Ins); zaung-ya (Bur); Balimbing (Phi); ma fuang (Tha); khe (Vie).

Description: Small, usually much branched tree, to 15 m tall. Bushy growth, usually with drooping branches. 3-6 pairs of 4-10 cm long, ovate leaflets and a single terminal leaflet. Flowers normally in auxiliary panicles, with joined petals, up to 8 mm in length, light red with purple centre. Fruit 12 x 6 cm, shiny yellow-green when ripe, with 5 pronounced ribs. Many cultivars. Flower and fruit all the year round.

Use: As *A. bilimbi*. Fruit also used fresh in salads, drinks, jam and jelly.

Ecology and Distribution: Like *A. bilimbi* but extends to frost free subtropical areas. More often commercially grown.

References: Purseglove (1974), Smitinand & Larsen (1981), Verheij & Coronel (1991).

Key characteristics: Low branches; inner bark pink and astringent; pinnately compound leaves; leaflet margin undulate; flowers small, white, fragrant.

Azadirachta indica

Meliaceae

Synonyms: *Melia indica, Melia azadirachta*

Common names: Neem, margosa-tree (En); mind (Ins); tamaka (Bur); mambu, sadu (Mal); kwinin, sadao India (Tha); sàu-dâu (Vie). var. siamensis: kadao, sadao, cha-tang (Tha).

Description: Up to 20 m high and 1 m in trunk diameter, with low branches and dense rounded crown. Bark brown when young, then grey with deep furrows and scaly plates. Inner bark pink, astringent and bitter tasting. Leaves pinnately compound (usually without single terminal leaflet) and may fall during severe drought. Each leaf has 9-17 pairs of 4-8 cm long curved, lance shaped, saw-toothed and pointed leaflets. Flowers are abundant, small, white and fragrant, arising in the corner of leaf stalks. Fruits are small, smooth ellipsoidal drupes, yellow or greenish-yellow when ripe.

Use: Windbreak, shade and fodder tree for cattle, soil improvement and wasteland reclamation. Wood is insect repellant and used for construction, furniture, paper pulp, chipboard and fuelwood. Azadirachtin, an insecticidal compound can be extracted from the seeds and leaves.

Ecology: Thrives in a wide range of soils, temperatures and rainfall patterns and is found on poor soils from sea level to 1,500 m elevation surviving temperatures from below 0°C to over 40°C and annual rainfall down to 130 mm. Prefers acid soils, warm temperatures and from 450 to 1,500 mm of rainfall.

Distribution: Native to dry regions from the Indian subcontinent through Burma, Thailand and Malaysia to Indonesia.

References: F/FRED (1992), Hensleigh & Holaway (1988), National Research Council (1980, 1992).

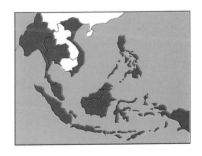

Baccaurea ramiflora

B. racemosa (Not illustrated)
Key characteristics: Small tree, leaves glandular, flowers & fruits on large branches or trunk.

B. ramiflora
Key characteristics: +/- buttresses; leaves ovate to ovate lance shaped; leaf stalk to 8 cm.

Baccaurea racemosa

Euphorbiaceae

Synonyms: *Baccaurea wallichii*

Common names: Kapundung (En); mente, kepundung (Ins, Mal); bencoy (Ins); jinteh merah.(Mal).

Description: 15-25m tall, 25-70cm in diameter with dense, irregular crown. Leaves simple, entire, ovate-oblong to obovate, 7-18cm long and 3-7cm wide, glandular, on 0.5-4.5cm long leaf stalks. Inflorescence on old branches or trunk. Male racemes 5-13cm long, with many 3-flowered densely haired cymes. Flowers small with 4-5 sepals and 4-8 stamens. Female racemes 10-20cm long, with larger flowers, 5 sepals and no petals. Fruits yellow-green or reddish, 2-2.4cm in diameter.

Use: Fruits eaten fresh, stewed, pickled or fermented. The excellent timber is used for house and boat construction and furniture making. Also used as support for rattan, as ornamental or as shade tree. Dyes is made from the bark.

Ecology: Native to tropical lowland forest up to 1,000 m altitude on a wide range of soils, from dry sandstone to peat swamps.

Distribution: Originates in western Malesia and widely cultivated in Java, Sumatra and Bali.

Baccaurea ramiflora

Synonyms: *Baccaurea sapida*, *B. wrayi*

Common names: Burmese grape (En); phnkiew (Cam); mafai setambun, tajam molek (Ins); f'ai (Lao); pupor, tampoi, tempui (Mal); kanazo (Bur); mafai, omfai, hamkang (Tha); giau gia dat, giau tien, dzau mien dzu'ó'i (Vie).

Description: Tree up to 25m high sometimes with buttresses. Leaves alternate, simple, ovate to ovate-lanceolate, 10-20cm long and 4-9cm wide with 1-8cm long petioles. Inflorescence on branches and trunk, soft-hairy, male racemes 3-8 cm long, female racemes 14cm long. 4-5 sepals. Fruits 2.5-3cm in diameter, smooth, yellowish pink to bright red.

Ecology and Use: As *B. racemosa*. Bark is used in traditional medicine.

Distribution: Burma, Thailand, southern China, Indo-China and peninsular Malaysia.

References: Verheij & Coronel (1992).

Key characteristics: Small, bushy tree, green to red stem, young twigs rust colored, ovate to heart-shaped leaves, large pink-white flowers, rambutan-like fruit.

Bixa orellana Bixaceae

Common names: Annato (En); thidin (Bur); achuete (Phi); kham ngoh (Tha); dièu-nhuôm, siêm phung (Vie).

Description: A small bushy tree, 2-8 m tall and up to 30 cm in diameter. Bark color varying from green to red, young twigs with rust colored scales. Leaves alternate, ovate or heart-shaped, 8-20 cm long and 5-12 cm wide. Flowers pink or white, 5-8 cm in diameter with 5-7 obovate petals. Fruit green to dark red, 2-4 cm, fleshy and spined – resembling rambutan. Seed pods brown with 10-50 bright orange to yellowish-red seeds.

Use: Often used as an ornamental or as living fences. Stem and branches cen be used for firewood. Seeds are traded commercially as a dyeing agent for food, particularly cheese and butter, leather, floor polish and cloth. The bark and leaves have various medicinal uses.

Ecology: Lowland tropical species occurring up to 800 m altitude. Prefers moist deep, loamy soil but is adaptable. Tolerates mild droughts, shorter than 4 months.

Distribution: Originates in tropical America and now widely distributed in the tropics, including Burma, Thailand, Cambodia, Vietnam, Malaysia, Indonesia and the Philippines.

References: Guzman et al (1986), Hensleigh & Holaway (1988).

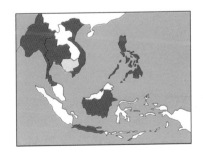

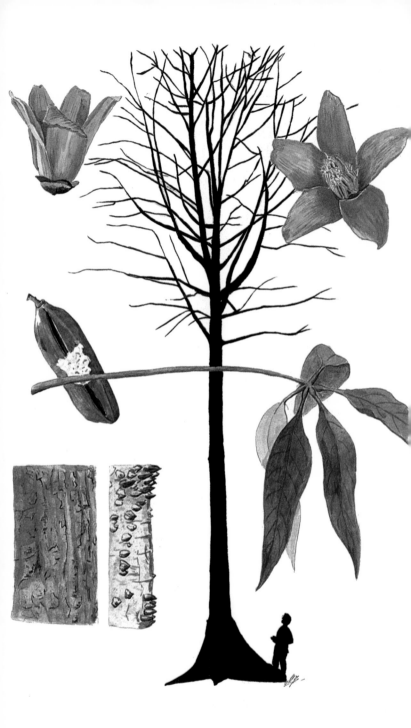

Key characteristics: Sometimes spines on stem; horizontal branches, palmately compound leaves, large red flowers, seed capsules with silky /hairy fill.

Bombax ceiba   Bombacaceae

Synonyms: *Salmalia malabarica*, *Bombax malabaricum*

Common names: Silk cotton tree, red cotton tree (En); letpan (Bur); ngiu baan (Tha); malabulak (Phi).

Description: A large deciduous tree up to 40 m tall and 80 cm in diameter, often with buttresses. Branches in regular whorls. Bark light brown or greyish and fairly smooth. Young stem and branches are covered with large conical thorns. Leaves palmately compound of 5-7 oblong-lanceolate, pointed leaflets, 10-20 cm long, leathery and smooth. Leaf stalks longer than leaflets. The flowers are 8-10 cm long, red, occurring at or near end of branches, appearing before the leaves. The fruit is a cylindrical pointed capsule, 12 to 17 cm long with numerous seeds inside embedded in silky material.

Use: Silky material around seeds is used as stuffing (kapok) but of lower quality than Ceiba pentandra. Bark is used for rope making. Wood can be used packing cases, toys, matches, canoes and others. Young flowers can be eaten as a vegetable. Flowers, pods, roots and gum are used in traditional medicine.

Ecology: Tropical humid lowland species, often found near stream banks.

Distribution: From India to the Philippines, including Burma and Thailand.

References: Guzman et al (1986), Storrs (1990).

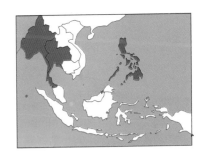

Key characteristics: Angular or flattened, hanging branchlets; leaves often large, forming dense foliage; flowers small, 4-merous; fruits yellow-orange looking like small mangoes.

Bouea macrophylla

Anacardiaceae

Synonyms: *Bouea gandaria*

Common names: Gandaria (En); ramania, gandaria (Ins); kundang, rembunia, setar (Mal); ma praang, somprang (Tha).

Description: Up to 27 m tall tree with light brown, fissured bark. Branchlets often smooth, hanging and angular or flattened. Leaves ovate-oblong to lance shaped or elliptic, simple, entire, papery and shining , up to 45 cm long and 13 cm wide, but usually smaller. Leaf base acute to cuneate and leafstalk 1-2.5 cm long. The leaves form a quite dense foliage. Inflorescences are 4-12 cm long panicles with mostly 4-merous, yellowish flowers turning brown. The yellow-orange fruits are mango-like, roundish, 2.5-5 cm in diameter, fleshy-juicy, sour to sweet in taste with faint turpentine smell.

Use: The ripe fruit is eaten fresh, cooked in syrup, or made into compote. The young fruit is used in chili based condiment ("sambal") and in pickles, the young violet leaves sometimes being eaten along with the sambal.

Ecology: Thrives in light fertile soils in the humid tropics from lowland to 300 m altitude where it occurs naturally. Cultivated up to 850 m altitude.

Distribution: Occurs naturally in Malaysia and Indonesia and is also cultivated in Thailand.

References: Verheij & Coronel (1992).

Key characteristics: Bush; leaves with 3 leaflets - grey beneath; finely haired; yellow flowers; pods 4-7 cm x 1 cm with 2-7 seeds.

Trees and Fruits of Southeast Asia

Cajanus cajan

Synonyms: *Cajanus indicus, Cajan cajan, Cajanus bicolor*

Common names: Pigeon pea, cajan, red gram (En); pe-sinngon (Bur); thua maetaai, thua rae, ma hae (Tha); kadios (Phi).

Description: Erect woody shrub of varying shape, 1-5 m high, branched and fine-haired. Stem and branches smooth and green. Leaves trifoliate with oblanceolate, pointed, hairy, 3-10 cm long leaflets, greyish beneath. Flowers are 1.5 cm long, yellow, sometimes with red stripe. The pods are 4 to 10 cm long and 1 cm wide, hairy, pointed and contains 2-7 seeds.

Use: Green pods and seeds used as vegetable and animal feed. Dried husks are also used for animal feed. Dried stalks and branches used for fuel and branches also for thatch and baskets. Leaves are fed to livestock, silkworms and lac insects or used as green manure. Also planted as windbreak and for erosion control. An enzyme called "urease" used medically, can be extracted from pigeon pea.

Ecology: Adapted to the arid and subhumid tropics. Grows in full sun on nearly any kind of soil, except waterlogged, but prefers neutral, light, deep loam or sandy soil, temperatures between 18 and 29°C, and rainfall between 600 and 1,000 mm. Tolerates as little as 400 mm annual rain and a dry season of 6 months.

Distribution: Grown all around the tropical world between 30ES and 30EN.

References: F/FRED (1992), Hensleigh & Holaway (198.), Purseglove (1974).

Key characteristics: Shrub or small tree; 3-5 crooked stems; black-brown bark; leaves bipinnate, dark green; flowers puff-ball like, reddish-purplish; fruit pods curving back as they split open.

Calliandra calothyrsus

Leguminosae
(Mimosoideae)

Synonyms: *Calliandra confusa, C. similis*

Common names: Calliandra (En, Bur, Phi); kaliandra (Ins).

Description: A small tree or shrub from 1.5-12 m tall, with 3-5 or more crooked stems up to 30 cm in diameter with black-brown bark. Leaves alternate, dark green, bipinnate and 10-17 cm long, with 15-20 pairs of lateral axes (pinnae), 4-7 cm long. Each axis has 25 to 60 pairs of linear leaflets, 5-8 mm long and 1 mm wide. The puffball-like flowers are in pyramid shaped, subterminal clusters and have long red or purple stamens. The fruit pods are 8-11 cm long and 1 cm wide, curving back as they split open.

Use: Mainly used for fuelwood and charcoal. Foliage is used as fodder and green manure and because it flowers year round it is popular as a honey tree.

Ecology: Thrives in tropical temperatures, from slightly elevated to 1,500 m altitude, with at least 1,000 mm annual rainfall, but prefers 2,000-4,000 mm. Tolerates 3-6 month dry season. Prefers light, well drained, slightly acidic soils and tolerates poor exhausted soils but not waterlogging. Nitrogen fixing.

Distribution: Native to central and southern America and widely cultivated in Indonesia. Also found in Burma, the Philippines, and other countries.

References: Hensleigh & Holaway (1988), Little (undated); National Research Council (1983); Westphal & Jansen (1993).

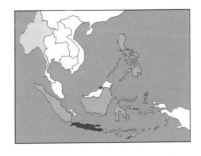

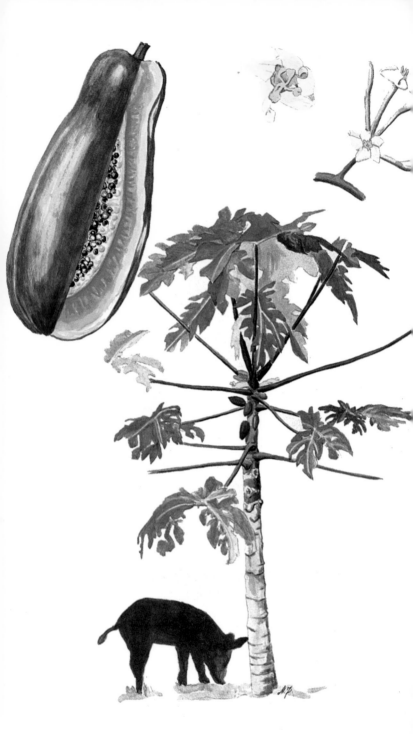

Key characteristics: Normally unbranched straight stem with "umbrella" of large characteristic leaves at top, white to yellow flowers and large green to yellow fruits year round.

Carica papaya Caricaceae

Common names: Papaya, pawpaw, melon tree (En); ihong, doeum lahong (Cam); papaya, gedang, kates (Ins); houng (Lao); papaya, betek, ketalah (Mal); thimbaw (Bur); papaya, kapaya, lapaya (Phi); malakor, loko, ma kuai thet (Tha); du du (Vie).

Description: A fast growing tree-like herb, 10-30 cm in diameter and 2 to 10 m high. Usually no branches, but if top is cut off, it will branch. Leaves spirally arranged, clustered towards top of stem, with up to 1 m long leaf stalks and palmate or deeply lobed leaf plates 25-75 cm in diameter, smooth, prominently veined and toothed. Flowers cream white to yellow, male, female or hermaphrodite on separate trees and looking somewhat different. The fruit is a fleshy berry 7-30 cm long and weighing up to 10 kg. Skin thin, smooth, turning from green to yellowish or orange when ripening. Flesh yellow to orange, soft, edible and sweet, with grey-black seeds along central cavity.

Use: The ripe fruit is eaten fresh or used in salads, drinks, jam, candies. The green fruit can be cooked as a vegetable. Young leaves and flowers are also eaten in some areas. Carpaine, an alkaloid and papaine, an enzyme, are extracted for use in pharmaceutical, beverage and food industries.

Ecology: Tolerates any kind of well drained and not too dry soil, but is very sensitive to waterlogging and flooding. Thrives in warm areas with sufficient rainfall and temperature range of 21-33°C and occurs up to about 1,600 m altitude above where frosts may occur.

Distribution: Originates in tropical America but is now distributed throughout the tropical and warm subtropical world.

References: Hensleigh & Holaway (1988), Purseglove (1974), Verheij & Coronel (1991).

Key characteristics: Bark greenish when young later reddish brown, peeling of in scales; compound leaves; flowers large, yellow and abundant; fruit pods cylindrical to 30 cm long or more.

Cassia fistula
Leguminosae (Caesalpinioideae)

Common names: Golden shower (En); ngu, ngu sahwe, pwabet (Bur); khuun, rajaphruek (Tha); bò-cap nuóc (Vie).

Description: A small to moderate sized tree up to 15 m tall. Bark greenish grey when young later turning reddish brown and peeling of in scales. Compound leaves 30-60 cm long on 7-10 cm long stalk, with 3-8 pairs of leathery leaflets, each about 12 cm long and 6 cm wide. The attractive flowers are large and yellow and borne in hanging racemes. The fruit pods are 30 to 60 cm long, cylindrical, smooth and dark brown when ripe.

Use: The wood is used for buildings, carts, fence posts and agricultural implements as well as for charcoal. The bark is also used for dyeing and tanning and the pods are used in traditional medicine.

Ecology: Grows from sea level up to about 1,200 m altitude.

Distribution: From India and Nepal through Burma, Thailand, Laos, Cambodia, China, Vietnam and Indonesia.

References: Smitinand & Larsen (1984), Storrs (1990).

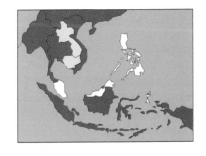

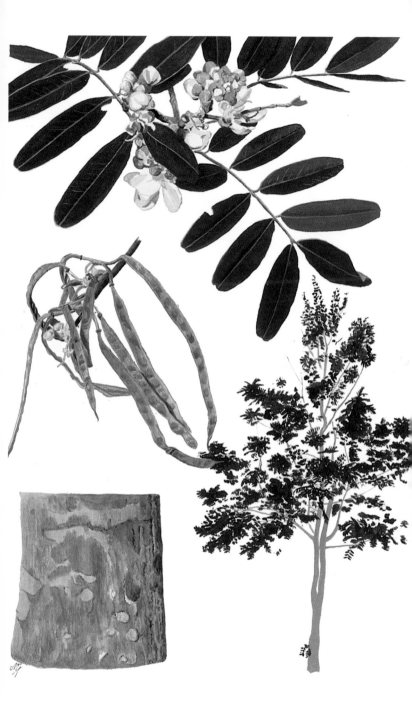

Key characteristics: Medium sized tree with grey bark and pinnately compound leaves, usually 7-10 pairs of leaflets, each
up to 8 cm long. Large clusters of bright yellow flowers and
clusters of long flat seed pods.

Cassia siamea

Leguminosae
(Caesalpinioideae)

Synonyms: *Cassia florida*

Common names: Yellow cassia, kassod tree, kassaof tree, Bombay blackwood (En); mezali (Bur); minjri, moung, angkank (Phi); khi lek, pak chili (Tha); muòng xiêm (Vie).

Description: A medium-sized tree, rarely exceeding 20 m in height and 50 cm in diameter at breast height (1.3 m above the ground). Dense evergreen spreading crown and smooth greyish bark. Young branches finely haired. Leaves are pinnately compound with even leaf arrangement of 7 to 10 pairs. Leaflets ovate-oblong, 7-8 cm long and 1-2 cm wide. Flowers are yellow and arise in large clusters and the fruit is a long flat pod with numerous seeds.

Use: Erosion control, windbreaks, shade. Wood is used for furniture, poles and fuelwood. Leaves can be eaten by ruminants. Young leaves and flowers used in curry dishes.

Ecology: Occurs naturally in dry lowland forests with average temperatures between 20 and 28°C and is very light demanding. Grows best in light, deep, well-drained and rich soils but may tolerate lateritic or limestone soils if well-drained. Most common in areas with annual rainfall of 650 mm or more and a dry season of 4 to 6 months.

Distribution: Native in southeast Asia and found in most countries of the region.

References: F/FRED (1992), Hensleigh & Holaway (1988), Smitinand & Larsen (1981).

Key characteristics: Stem and branches with conical spines. Branches horizontal, leaves compound palmate, ripe fruits packed with whitish floss-kapok.

Ceiba pentandra

Bombacaceae

Synonyms: *Bombax pentandrum, Eriodendron anfractuosum*

Common names: Kapok, white silk-cotton tree (En); koo (Cam); kapok, randu, kapu (Ins); nguiz baanz (Lao); kabuk-abu, kakabu, pohon kapok (Mal); nun (Tha); gòn, gau (Vie).

Description: A fast growing, deciduous tree with straight bole, sometimes buttresses, reaching 30 m (var. *pentandra*) in height. Bole and branches more or less with conical spines. Branches horizontal, whorled in groups of 3, giving a pagoda-shaped thin crown. Leaves alternate, with 8-25 cm long petioles, palmately compound of 5-11 smooth, oblong-lanceolate leaflets, 5-16 cm long. The numerous flowers dirty white, about 3 cm long, with foetid milky smell, appearing in groups at the beginning of the dry season when trees are leafless. Fruits are ellipsoidal capsules, 7.5-30 cm long that becomes brown when ripe and opens with 5 valves. Seeds are embedded in copious white, pale yellow or grey floss.

Use: Yields kapok, the floss in the fruits, which is used for stuffing and thermal and acoustic insulation. Very young, unripe pods are eaten in Java.

Ecology: Grows under a wide variety of conditions, but thrives better below 500 m elevation and with at least 1,000 mm annual rain, particular important during the vegetative growth period. Flowering and fruiting occurs during the dry season, but fruiting fails at night temperatures below 20°C.

Distribution: Wild varieties grow in tropical America and Africa. It was introduced in Asia centuries ago and is now reported cultivated in Burma, Thailand, Cambodia, Malaysia, Indonesia and the Philippines.

References: Purseglove (1974), Westphal & Jansen (1993).

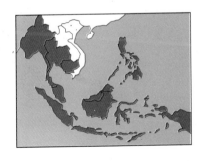

Key characteristics: Medium sized tree; white latex; leaves rust colored below; branchlets hairy; green yellow or purple fruits round, 5-10cm in diameter.

Chrysophyllum cainito

Sapotaceae

Common names: Cainito, starapple (En); sawo ijo, sawo hejo, sawo kadu (Ins); sawo duren, pepulut (Mal); hnin-thagya (Bur); caimito (Phi); chicle durian (Sin); sataa appoen (Tha); vú-sùe (Vie).

Description: An evergreen tree up to 35 m tall and 60 cm in diameter with white gummy latex. Branchlets numerous, with many brown hairs. Leaves alternate, oblong to obovate, 5-16 cm x 3-6 cm, leathery, rust red below and with almost parallel secondary nerves. Leaf margins thickened. Flowers arising from leaf corners on current season's shoots, in groups of 5-35 small yellow to purplish-white flowers with 5 sepals, 1-4 mm long. Fruit a berry, 5-10 cm in diameter, obovoid-globose, yellow-green or purplish brown with thin leathery skin and white or purple, soft juicy flesh.

Use: Fruit can be eaten fresh or used in ice cream. Bark, latex and fruit and seeds have medicinal value. Wood is suitable for construction and branches are used as an orchid growing medium. Also planted as an ornamental.

Ecology: Grows well in most soil types and within a wide climatic range in lowland areas. Performs best where soil is fertile and well drained.

Distribution: Originates in tropical West Indies. In Southeast Asia most common in the Philippines, but also found in Burma, Thailand, Vietnam, Malaysia, Indonesia and Singapore.

References: Hensleigh & Holaway (1988), Verheij & Coronel (1992).

Citrus aurantiifolia

Citrus hystrix

C. aurantiifolia
Key characteristics: Dense, irregularly branched; short stiff spines; narrowly winged leaf stalks; fruit juicy, 3-6cm in diameter thin skin, acid.

C. hystrix
Key characteristics: Crooked trunk; short stiff spines; leaf stalk broadly winged; fruit with irregular bumpy skin.

Citrus aurantiifolia

Rutaceae

Synonyms: *Limonia aurantifolia*, *Citrus javanica*, *C. notissima*

Common names: Lime, sour lime (En); krôôch chmaa muul (Cam); jeruk nipis, jeruk pecel (Ins); naaw (Lao); limau ni-pis, limau asam (Mal); dayap (Phi); som manao, manao (Tha); chanh ta (Vie).

Description: Dense, irregularly branched, to 5m tall. Short stiff spines on twigs. Leaves alternate, elliptic to oblong-ovate, 4-8cm long, 2-5cm wide with narrowly winged leaf stalks, crenulate margin. 1-7 small white flowers in each stand from leaf corners, with 4-6 petals and 20-25 stamens. Fruit round, greenish-yellow, 3-6 cm in diameter with thin skin. Flesh yellow-green, juicy, fragrant, very acid. Seeds small, ovoid and pale.

Use: The fruit is extensively used to flavor food and drinks and for various medicinal purposes. Leaves are also used in traditional medicine.

Ecology: Lowland tropical species found up to about 1,000 m altitude. Sensitive to cold and waterlogging but tolerates some drought and poor soils.

Distribution: Cultivated in all Southeast Asian countries.

Citrus hystrix

Rutaceae

Synonyms: *Citrus macroptera*

Common names: Mauritius papeda, leech-lime (En); krauch soeuch (Cam); jeruk perut, limo purut (Ins); 'khi 'hout (Lao); limau purut (Mal); shouk-pote (Bur); kabuyau, kulubut, kolobot (Phi); ma kruut (Tha); trùc (Vie).

Description: Up to 12m in height, with crooked trunk and short stiff spines. Leaves broadly ovate to ovate-oblong, 3-15cm long, 2-6cm wide with cuneate or rounded base and broadly winged stalk. Flowers small, fragrant and yellowish white. Fruits ovoid to elliptical, 5-7cm in diameter, green to yellow with irregular bumpy skin and very acid.

Use: Used like the common lime as well as for insecticides (juice) and a flavoring agent (leaves).

Ecology: Low to medium altitudes in the tropics.

Distribution: Origin not known. Has become naturalized in Malaysia, Indonesia and Burma and is also found in Thailand and the Philippines.

References: Guzman et al (1986), Verheij & Coronel (1992).

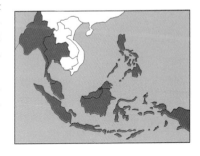

Key characteristics: Small tree, low spreading branches, some-times spines, young parts with fine soft hairs, leaves with glan-dular dots and broadly winged leaf stalks, large whitish fra-grant flowers, very large round fruit.

Citrus maxima

Rutaceae

Synonyms: *Citrus aurantium* var *grandis*, *C. grandis*, *C. decumana*

Common names: Pummelo, shaddock, pomelo (En); krôoch thlông (Cam); jeruk besar, jeruk bali (Ins); kiéngz s'aangz, ph'uk, sômz 'ôô (Lao); jambua, limau betawi, limau bali (Mal); shouk-ton-oh, kywegaw (Bur); som-o, ma-o (Tha); bu'o'i (Vie).

Description: A 5-15 m tall tree with low, spreading branches, with up to 5 cm long spines if propagated by seed. Vegetatively propagated trees usually spineless. Young parts with soft short hairs. Leaves glandular dotted, ovate to elliptical, 5-10 (-2) m long and 2-5 (-12) cm wide, with entire to shallowly crenate margin, rounded to sub-cordate base, obtusely acute leaf tip and broadly winged leaf stalks, up to 7 cm wide. One or a few large creamy white flowers arising from corner of leaf stalks (axillary), 3-5 cm wide, 5-merous, 20-25 stamens. Fruits are round to pear-shaped, 10-30 cm in diameter, greenish-yellow with dense glandular dots and 1-3 cm thick peel. Fruit "flesh" pale yellow or pink, sweet, juicy and with a few large seeds.

Use: Mainly grown for the fruit, which is eaten fresh or in salads or made into juice. In Vietnam the flowers are used for perfume. The wood can be used for tool handles. Leaves, flowers, fruit and seeds are used for various medicinal purposes (including against coughs, fevers and stomach disorders).

Ecology: Lowland tropical species grown commercially up to 400 m altitude. Although it tolerates a wide range of soils, it prefers deep, medium textured fertile soils free from salt. In Thailand pomelo grows at mean monthly temperatures of 25-30°C and annual rainfall at about 1,500-1,800 mm, with a few cooler and dryer months.

Distribution: Indigenous to Malesian region, but exact origin uncertain. Now found in all countries in Southeast Asia and also outside the region.

References: Verheij & Coronel (1992).

Citrus reticulata

Citrus sinensis

C. reticulata
Key characteristics: Small; slender spiny twigs; leaves small, narrow, glandular; narrowly winged leaf stalks; small white flowers; ripe fruit orange color, loose peel.

C. sinensis
Key characteristics: <15m high; spiny; young twigs angular; narrowly winged leaf stalks; fruit round, 4-12cm in diameter, yellow green or orange. Seeds white inside.

Citrus reticulata

Rutaceae

Synonyms: *Citrus nobilis, C. deliciosa, C. chrysocarpa*

Common names: Mandarin, tangerine (En); krauch kvich (Cam); jeruk ke-prok, jeruk jepun, jeruk maseh (Ins); som hot, som lot, liou (Lao); limau langkat, limau kupas, limau wangkas (Mal); leinmaw (Bur); som khieo waan, som saenthong, ma baang (Tha); cam sành, cay quit (Vie).

Description: A small, usually spiny tree up to 8m tall. Twigs slender. Leaves lanceolate or elliptic, 4-8cm long, 1.5-4cm wide, acute tip and base, usually crenate, dark shiny green above, yellow-green below. Leaf stalk narrowly winged or margin-ed. Small white flowers single or in small groups at leaf corners, 1.5-2.5cm in diameter, 5 petals. Fruit a depressed roundish berry with thin, loose peel, orange when ripe. Pulp orange, sweet and juicy. Seeds small, green embryo inside. Many cultivars.

Use: Fruit consumed fresh, canned or as juice. Pectin, essential oils in rind.

Ecology: Grown between 45EN and 45ES with different cultivars having different requirements. Prefers cooler climates with a dry season.

Distribution: Originates in Malesia but is now strongly differentiated and very widely distributed in all tropical and subtropical parts of the world.

Citrus sinensis

Synomyms: *Citrus aurantium var. sinensis*

Common names: Sweet orange (En); krôôch pôôsat (Cam); jeruk manis (Ins); kièngz (Lao); limau manis, chula, choreng (Mal); thung chin-thi (Bur); kahel (Phi); somkliang, somtra (Tha); cam (Vie).

Description: 6-15m tall, evergreen. Young twigs angular. Leaves alternate, elliptic to ovate, 5-15cm long, 2-8cm wide, 1-3cm long narrowly winged stalk, rounded base, undulate to crenate margin, pointed tip. White 5-merous flowers single or in racemes at leaf corners, 2-3cm in diameter, fragrant. Fruit round, 4-12cm in diameter, yellow-green to orange with up to 5 mm thick glandular peel. Flesh juicy, yellow to orange-red, sweet to slightly acid. Seeds, white inside.

Use: Like mandarin. Pulp, molasses used as cattle feed.

Ecology: Subtropical. Prefers seasonal changes. Quality and yield is lower in the lowlands.

Distribution: Thought to originate near China-Vietnam border and now cultivated everywhere in the subtropics and tropics.

References: Purseglove (1974), Verheij & Coronel (1992).

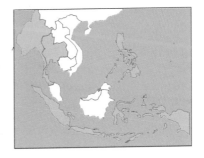

Coffea arabica

Coffea canephora

C. arabica
Key characteristics: Up to 5 m tall; leaves opposite, 8-15 cm long; ripe berries red or yellow.

C. caneophora
Key characteristics: Bush or small tree; leaves 15-30cm long, opposite, with undulating margin, prominent midrib below.

Coffea arabica Rubiaceae

Common names: Arabica (En); Coffee in general: kafae (Cam, Lao); kopi (Ins, Mal); ka-phi (Bur); kafe (Phi); gafae (Tha); cà phê (Vie).

Description: 4-5m tall. Horizontal branches in opposite pairs. Leaves opposite, dark green, shiny, 5-15cm long, 6cm wide, oval or elliptical, pointed, sometimes undulating. Flowers white, 2-20 together in leaf corners. Red or yellow berries oblong, 15mm long.

Use: For coffee production. Dried pulp used in livestock food, for cottage soap production and fertilizer.

Ecology: In its native habitat it grows at 1,300-1,800m altitude, prefers temperature between 13-24°C (not below zero) and annual rainfall of about 1,900mm, but will grow with as little as 750mm a year if evenly distributed. A short mild drought facilitates uniform flowering. Prefers deep, slightly acid, fertile and well drained soils.

Distribution: Native to Ethiopian mountains but now found in most southeast Asian countries, including Burma, Thailand, Indonesia and the Philippines.

Coffea canephora

Synonyms: *Coffea robusta, C. laurentii, C. maclaudii, C. arabica* var. *stuhlmani, C. bukobensis, C. welwitschii, C. ugandae, C. kouilouensis.*

Common names: Robusta coffee (En).

Description: Umbrella-shaped shrub or small tree, up to 10m tall. In full light branching near base. Leaves opposite, 15-30cm long, 5-15cm wide, often corrugated or undulating, oblong-elliptic, shortly pointed tip, base rounded or broadly cuneate, midrib flat above, prominent below, 8-13 pairs of lateral veins. Leaf stalk 0.8-2cm long with 5mm long triangular scale-like appendage at base. Flowers from leaf corners, usually 6 together of which 3-4 develops. Flowers white, fragrant. Corolla tube about 1cm long and the 5-7 lobes 1-1.5cm long. Fruit round, 1.2cm in diameter, green to crimson to black.

Use: Lower quality than arabica, mainly used in coffee blends and for "instant" coffee.

Ecology: Grows from sea level to about 1,600m altitude. Prefers 1,100-2,500mm annual rainfall and 18-32EC. Dry season favourable for flower initiation.

Distribution: Burma, Thailand, Vietnam, Malaysia, Indonesia and the Philippines.

References: Hensleigh & Holaway (1988), Purse-glove (1974), Westphal & Jansen (1993).

Key characteristics: Short trunk; root-like buttresses; wide spreading umbrella shaped crown; about 25 pairs of leaflets per pinnae; abundant, showy red flowers; pods woody, flat, up to 40 cm long.

Delonix regia

Leguminosae
(Caesalpinioideae)

Synonym: *Poinciana regia*

Common names: Flamboyant, flame of the forest (En); seinban (Bur); hang nok yung farang (Tha); phuong (Vie).

Description: A small to moderate sized semi-deciduous tree up to 15 m tall with short trunk, often root-like buttresses and a wide, spreading, umbrella shaped crown reaching 15 m in diameter. The bark is smooth and grey with vertical lines of brown spots. The compound leaves are alternate, 20-60 cm long and divided into 15-25 pairs of pinnae, each of which has about 14-30 pairs of small, oblong leaflets, 8-10 mm long and 3-4 mm wide. The numerous showy red flowers with yellow margins grows in dense clusters sometimes almost entirely covering the crown. The fruit pods are stout, woody, reddish brown or black, flat and up to 40 cm long.

Use: Primarily an ornamental species widely planted along streets and in parks, gardens and villages.

Ecology: Grows in warm humid areas from sea level up to about 1,000 m altitude.

Distribution: From its origin in Madagascar, it has been introduced to most of Africa and Asia, including Burma, Thailand, Laos, Cambodia, Vietnam and the Philippines.

References: Smitinand & Larsen (1984), Storrs (1990).

Key characteristics: Dense short hairs on branches, ribs, veins of leaves & flower stands; leaves with 1-3 pairs of leaflets; fruits round, yellow-brown, 1-3 cm in diameter, translucent white edible flesh.

Dimocarpus longan   Sapindaceae

Synonyms: Subspecies longan and its varieties: var. longan:
Euphoria longana, *Nephelium longana*; var. longepetiolatus: *Euphoria morigera*; var. obtusus: *E. scandens*. For subspecies
malesianus: var. malesianus: *Nephelium malaiense*, *Euphoria cinerea*, *E. malaiensis*, *E. gracilis*; var. echinatus: *Euphoria
nephelioides*.

Common names: Ssp. longan var. longan: Longan (En); mien
(Cam); lengkeng (Ins, Mal); lam nhai (Lao); kyet mouk (Bur);
lamyai pa (Tha); nhan (Vie). -ssp. longan var. obtusus: lamyai
khruer, lamyai tao (Tha). -ssp. malesianus var. malesianus: Mata
kucing (peninsular Mal and Sabah); isau, sau, kakus (Sarawak);
buku, ihau, meduru (Ins).

Description: Up to 40 m high and 1m in diameter, sometimes with buttresses. Branches cylindrical in cross-section with
5 faint grooves and covered with dense short reddish-brown
hairs. Leaves with 1- 20 cm long petiole, hairy and 1-2 (sometimes 3) pairs of elliptical leaflets, 3-45 cm long and 1.5-20 cm
wide. Leaflets with dense short hairs on midribs and nerves
on underside. Flowers usually grouped in cymes of 1-5 yellow-brown flowers at tip of branches. Flower with 5 petals
1.5-6 x 0.6-2 mm sometimes densely wooly. Fruit 1-3 cm in
diameter, smooth to warty or granular, yellow-brown (some
varieties green). Seeds round, shining blackish-brown, envel-
oped in thin, translucent white flesh.

Use: Fruit is eaten fresh or canned. A drink can be prepared from
the dried flesh. Seeds is used in shampoo and seeds and flesh have
various medicinal purposes.

Ecology: A subtropical tree requiring a cool period for good flowering and fruiting, 1,500-2,000 mm annual rain and sandy soils.

Distribution: Ssp longan var. longan ▢ : Burma, S. China, Thailand. Ssp. longan var. obtusus
■ + ▢ : Indo-China. Ssp longan var. longepetiolulatus ▢ :
Vietnam. Ssp. malesianus var.
malesianus: All countries in region, Ssp. malesianus var.
echinatus ▨ : Borneo, Philippines.

References: Verheij & Coronel
(1991).

Key characteristics: Very large tree, up to 55 m tall, branch-less up to 20 m. Bark thin, grey, smooth; twigs, leaves and buds soft-haired; fruit with 5 wings (lobes), 2 lobes large, up to 14 x 3 cm with 3 parallel nerves.

Dipterocarpus alatus   Dipterocarpaceae

Synonym: *Dipterocarpus philipinensis*

Common names: Hairy-leafed apitong, apinau, ayamban (Phi); chhë: ti:ël bangku:ëy, chhë ti:ël ba:y, chhë: ti:ël tük (Cam); maiz nhang, nhanh khaw (Lao); kanyin-byu (Bur); yang-na (Tha); daafu rasi (Vie).

Description: A medium to large size tree up to 55 m tall and 150 cm in diameter, with a tall, straight and cylindrical bole, branchless for up to 20 m. Bark thin, greyish and smooth. Leaves narrowly ovate to elliptical-oblong, 9-25 cm long and 3.5-15 cm wide with cuneate to rounded base and acute tip, 11-18 (sometimes 20) pairs of secondary veins, sparsely soft-haired above and densely soft haired below. Leaf stalk 2.5-4.5 cm long with greyish-yellow soft haired scale-like appendages at base. Fruit usually with 5 wings (calyx lobes), two larger ones up to 14cm long x 3cm wide with three parallel nerves, and three shorter ones up to 1.2-1.4 cm long.

Use: A very important source of construction timber. The oil rich resin is sometimes tapped in Burma for various minor uses, including medicinal.

Ecology: Occurs along rivers up to 500 m altitude, where it is a rapid colonizer of alluvial soils. In the Philippines found in mixed dipterocarp forest at low and medium altitudes.

Distribution: Burma, Thailand, Cambodia, Laos, Vietnam and the Philippines.

References: FAO (1985), Soerianegara & Lemmens (1994).

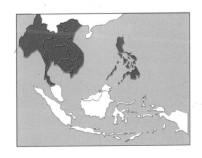

Key characteristics: Large tree; buttresses; dark red-brown bark, peeling off; silvery/golden scales and hair underneath leaves; flowering from old branches; large, spiny yellow green to brown fruit, strongly smelling.

Durio zibethinus Bombacaceae

Synonym: *Durio acuminatissima*

Common names: Durian (All languages); thu-réén (Cam); duren, ambetan, kadu (Ins); thurièn (Lao); thurian, rian (Tha); saù riêng (Vie).

Description: A large tree to 40 m tall, developing buttresses, with dark red-brown bark, peeling off irregularly. Leaves alternate, elliptical to lanceolate, 10-17 cm long and 3-12.5 cm wide, papery, with acute to obtuse base and slenderly pointed tip, smooth, glossy and densely reticulate above, densely covered with silvery or golden scales with a layer of stellate hairs below. Flowerstands on the older branches, forming fascicles of panicle-like groups (corymbs) each with 3-30 flowers, up to 15 cm long. Individual flowers 5-6 cm long, whitish or greenish-white, on 5-7 cm flower stalk, with 5 petals and numerous stamens in 5 bundles. Fruit a globose, ovoid or ellipsoid capsule, up to 25 cm long and 20 cm in diameter, yellow-green to brownish, covered with pyramidal, sharp, up to 1 cm long spines. The fruit opens in 5 thick valves wherein the up to 4 cm long seeds are embedded in yellowish, sweet aril with a smell described as a mixture of rotten cheese, garlic, turpentine and bad drains.

Use: Fruits are eaten fresh or processed into cakes, cookies and ice cream. Boiled or roasted seeds can be eaten as a snack and young shoots and unripe fruits may be cooked as greens. Dried fruit rind is used as fuel, in particular to smoke fish, and several parts are used medicinally. The coarse and light wood is sometimes used for indoor construction and lower quality furniture.

Ecology: A strictly tropical tree growing from sea level to 800 m altitude between 18°C and S, where rainfall is 1,500 mm per year and well distributed, and soils are deep, well drained and light.

Distribution: Native to Southeast Asia and cultivated in all countries covered by this guide.

References: Purseglove (1974), Verheij & Coronel (1992).

Erythrina variegata

Erythrina poeppigiana

Erythrina orientalis

Key characteristics: Thorny trunk and branches; trifoliate leaves; large red flowers before leaves appear; *Orientalis*: Short brown, black-tipped thorns; greyish green bark; *Poeppigiana*: Larger tree; bark greyish or greenish brown, warty, thorns larger; *Variegata*: Small, black thorns.

Erythrina orientalis, E. poeppigiana & E. variegata

Leguminosae (Papilionoideae)

Synonyms: Orientalis: *Erythrina indica*, *E. variegata* var. orientalis. Poeppigiana: *E. micropteryx*. Variegata: *E. indica*.

Common names: *E. orientalis*: Dapdap (Phi). *Poeppigiana*: Coral tree (En). *Variegata*: Tall erythrina, tall wiliwili, Indian coral tree, Chochin China coral tree (En); mottled leaf dapdap (Phi); thong baan, thong laang daang (Tha).

Description: *Orientalis*: Up to 15m tall. Stout branches and branchlets. Short dark-brown, black-tipped thorns. Bark greyish green, finely fissured. Alternate, trifoliate leaves on 20-40cm long leafstalk with entire, broadly ovate, somewhat acuminate leaflets, 8-18cm long, the terminal leaflet largest. Flowers in up to 25cm long, terminal racemes, with numerous large, bright red flowers with 4 cm long calyx and 7-9cm long petals. Pods are 10-25cm x 1.5-2cm. Often leafless during flowering.

Poeppigiana: Up to 40m tall and 120 cm in diameter with spreading crown. Bark greyish or greenish brown with smooth, slightly furrowed, warty or thorny surface. Leaves alternate, trifoliate, 20-30cm long. Leaflets 6-18cm long and 5-15cm wide, very thin with entire margin, short pointed tip and broadly pointed to straight base. Flowers in 10-20cm long racemes, orange-red, 3.5-5cm long and 1.7-2.5cm wide. Pods dark brown, cylindrical and straight, pointed in both ends, 12-25cm x 1.6cm, on a long stalk. Seeds bean like, 1.2-1.6cm x 0.5-0.7cm.

Variegata: Up to 20m tall, open branched tree with 1-2mm long small black thorns on trunk and branches. Leaves trifoliate, 13-18cm x 7.5-13cm, deciduous during water scarcity. Flowers orange-red, 5-7cm long and 2-3cm wide, mainly borne near top of the tree. Seed pods 8-13cm x 1.2cm with 2-3 dark brown seeds inside.

Use: Shade tree for coffee and cacao plantations and livestock, support trees for climbing crops and used as ornamental. The wood of *E. oientalis* is used for fishing net floats, insulation boards and other lightweight wood products. *E. poeppigiana* is also used as soil improver in pastures and its leaves are used as cattle feed or green manure and for various medicinal purposes. *E. variegata* is used as windbreak in the Pacific and the bark is used in traditional medicine.

Ecology: Nitrogen fixing. *E. orientalis* and variegata common in low to medium altitude tropical and sub-tropical coastal areas. *E. poeppigiana* is found along streams and in swamps, often in pure stands, up to 1,900 m altitude. *E. variegata* prefers 1,500-2,500mm annual rainfall but can survive with as little as 200mm.

Distribution: *E. orientalis* found from India to Polynesia, incl. Vietnam, Malaysia, Indonesia and the Philippines. *E. poeppigiana* is native to S. America, but has been introduced to S.E. Asia. *E. variegata* is native to New Caledonia but now naturalized from east Africa throughout southeast Asia and the Pacific, incl. Burma, Thailand, Indochina and the Philippines.

References: Guzman et al (1986); Hensleigh & Holaway (1988).

Key characteristics: Crooked bole, narrow lanceolate leaves and smooth often pinkish bark.

Trees and Fruits of Southeast Asia

Eucalyptus camaldulensis — Myrtaceae

Synonym: *Eucalyptus rostrata*

Common names: River red gum, red gum (En); pyilon-chantha (Bur).

Description: A small to medium-sized tree up to 20 m (may sometimes reach 45 m). Trunk often crooked, with smooth bark that can appear white, grey, brown or pinkish red, sometimes with air roots. Twigs long, slender, angled and reddish. Leaves alternate, ovate to broadly lanceolate when young, but more narrow lanceolate when older. 8-30 cm long and 1-2 cm wide, pointed, green to green-grey, with 12-15 mm long petiole. Inflorescence from leaf corners, with 7-11 white to cream-white flowers. Fruits 5-8 mm in diameter. Considerable morphological variation. Several varieties.

Use: Wood used for pulp, firewood (including charcoal) and construction where strength and durability is required. Flowers can produce first grade honey. Gum (kino) from bole can be used as dye. Widely planted in agroforestry systems (especially newer systems).

Ecology: In its natural habitat mainly found along watercourses up to 600 m altitude.

Distribution: Naturally wide-spread throughout northern Australia. Now widely introduced to most countries in S.E. Asia, including Burma, Thailand, Vietnam, Malaysia, Indonesia and the Philippines.

References: Hensleigh & Holoway (1988), Little (undated), NAC (1980), Soerianegara & Lemmens (1994).

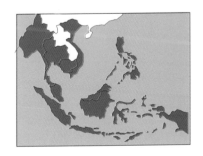

Key characteristics: Large straight tree with smooth, flaking brightly multicolored bark, sometimes buttresses. Twigs square in cross section and petioles twisted.

Trees and Fruits of Southeast Asia

Eucalyptus deglupta

Myrtaceae

Synonyms: *Eucalyptus multiflora, E. naudiniana, E. schlecteri*

Common names: Mindanao gum, deglupta (En); leda, galang, aren (Ins); bagras, banikag, amamanit (Phi).

Description: A very large evergreen tree up to 70 m high and 2.4 m in diameter, often with buttresses. Bark smooth, peeling off. Fresh exposed surface green, then gradually turns blue, purple and finally yellow or red. Twigs square with young leaves opposite, but older leaves may become alternate. Leaves ovate to ovate-lanceolate, held almost horizontal on branches, round to acute or somewhat pointed, slightly leathery, 7.5-15 cm x 5-7.5 cm, with twisted leaf stalks, aromatic when crushed. Inflorescence in leaf axils and at tip of twigs, 3-7 white flowers in each. Fruit round with pointed tip, 3-3.5 mm in diameter.

Use: General purpose timber and pulp, veneer, plywood, particle board, hardboard, wood-wool board as well as firewood.

Ecology: Prefer non-stagnant river flats with adequate soil moisture. In native distribution found from sea level to 1,800 m altitude.

Distribution: Widely planted throughout region, including Burma, Thailand, Malaysia, Indonesia (Sulawesi, Seram) and the Philippines.

References: Guzman et al (1986), Soerianegara & Lemmens (1994).

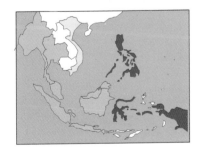

Key characteristics: Large tree; straight bole; white, grey-white or blue-grey smooth bark, flaky at base; mature leaves lanceolate.

Eucalyptus grandis
Myrtaceae

Common names: Flooded gum, rose gum (En); shan-tabye (Bur).

Description: A medium to very large tree, up to 55 m tall with a straight bole, branchless up to 30 m and up to 200 cm in diameter. Bark smooth, roughly flaky at base, white, grey-white or blue-grey in color. Twigs slender, angled and with white waxy coating. Leaves alternate, ovate when young, later lanceolate, 10-20 cm long and 2-3 cm wide with 1.5-2 cm leaf stalk. Inflorescence single with 7-11 flowers in each stand. Fruit more or less pear-shaped, 4-8 mm in diameter with 4-5 valves.

Use: The wood is especially used for boat building, flooring, plywood, panelling and general construction.

Ecology: Grows in moist subtropical lowlands, preferring deep, well drained and fertile soils.

Distribution: Native to coastal areas of southern Queensland and northern New South Wales and introduced to West Malaysia and Burma.

References: Little (undated), Soerianegara & Lemmens (1994).

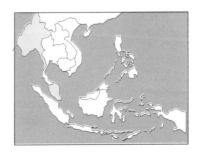

Ficus
heteropoda

Ficus
bengalensis

Ficus religiosa

Key characteristics: Short, thick, irregular trunk; round or pear shaped "fruit" with the flowers on inside walls, often arising on trunk and major branches; often with white latex.

Ficus spp.   Moraceae

A large genus of primarily tropical trees common in rainforests, of which some species are planted and have religious importance

Common name: Fig tree (En).

Description: Mostly trees, with short, thick trunk, and often many air roots. Many species have thick, shiny leaves with pointed tips. The major characte-ristic is the flowerstand, which is round or vase-shaped and hollow with all the flowers sitting on the inside wall. A small opening at the top allows the pollinating insect to enter. The inflorescences/fruits arise from the trunk and branches. Many species of so-called "strangling figs" like F. bengalensis germinate and grow on other trees, eventually overgrowing and strangling and shading the host to death.

Use: The fruits of many species are edible and the wood of some species is used for fuel. Several species are cultivated as household ornamental plants (e.g. *F. elastica*, *F. benjamina*). *F. religiosa* is very common around Buddhist temples.

Ecology: Mostly tropical. Found in all countries of the region.

Distribution: The genus is represented globally, but the species examples shown here are found in the Asian region only.

References: Storrs (1990).

Key characteristics: Straight trunk; symmetric branches; pyramid-shaped crown; leaves opposite, short-stalked, thick leathery; flowers 4-merous; petals yellow-green with red edges.

Garcinia mangostana Guttiferae

Synonym: *Mangostana garcinia*

Common names: Mangosteen (En); manggis (Ins, Mal); mankhud (Lao); mingut (Bur); manggustan, manggis (Phi); Mangkhut (Tha); cay mang cut (Vie).

Description: A 6-25 m tall tree with a straight trunk, symmetric branches and pyramid-shaped crown. Leaves opposite with short stalks, oblong or elliptical, 15-25 cm long and 7-13 cm wide, thick leathery, entire, sharply pointed tip, smooth and olive green above and yellow green below, with a pale green central nerve and evenly spaced, many prominent side nerves. Flowers on short, thick stalk, alone or in pairs at tip of branchlets, about 5.5 cm in diameter with 4 sepals and 4 yellow green petals with red edges. The mangosteen fruit is a globose, smooth berry, 4-7 cm in diameter, dark purple when ripe, with the sepals remaining on the fruit. The "skin" is about 0.9 cm thick, purple with 0-3 big seeds embedded in the glossy white "flesh".

Use: The highly praised fruit is mostly eaten fresh and only occasionally preserved. The fruit rind is used as a dyeing agent, and also, together with the bark, have several applications in traditional medicine. The wood is dark red, heavy and very strong and used in carpentry.

Ecology: Thrives in high temperature and humidity in protected places in tropical areas, often found together with durian. A short dry spell stimulates flowering.

Distribution: Probably originated in Malaysia, but wild forms is unknown. Now cultivated in Burma, Thailand, Vietnam, Malaysia, Indonesia and the Philippines.

References: Verheij & Coronel (1992).

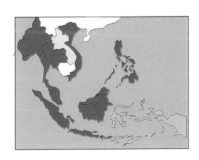

Key characteristics: Small tree with twisted trunk; green to grey bark; oddly bipinnately compound leaves with 8 or more pairs of leaflets, each 4-6 cm long. Fruit pods flat, light brown, 10-14 cm long and 2 cm wide.

Gliricidia sepium

Leguminosae (Papilionoideae)

Synonym: *Gliricidia maculata*

Common names: Quick stick (En); gamal (Ins); khê noyz, khê falang (Lao); thinbaw-ngusat (Bur); madre de cacao, kakauati (Phi); kha farang (Tha); hòng mai, sát-thu dóm (Vie).

Description: A small tree up to 10 m in height and 30 cm in diameter. Trunk twisted or angled with initially smooth green bark, later becoming greyish and covered with pores (lenticels). The leaves, which drop in cool or very dry periods, are alternate, oddly bipinnately compound, 15-30 cm long with 8 or more opposite pairs of leaflets, each 4-6 cm long, oblong ovate, pointed with rounded base. Inflorescences are numerous 4-8 cm long racemes, on leafless branches, with 2 cm long pink flowers with yellow and white. The pods are light brown, 10-14 cm long and 2 cm wide, flat and contains 6-8 seeds; they open suddenly, projecting the flat, disc shaped 7 mm diameter seeds with great force.

Use: Often used as living fence, shade for plantation crops, support for climbers, windbreak and erosion control and soil improvement. The hard durable wood can be used for fuel, furniture making, posts, tool handles and heavy construction.

Ecology: Grows in tropical climates with mean annual temperatures of 22-30°C from lowland to about 1,600 m altitude, receiving annual rainfall from minimum 1,000 mm to 2,300 mm. Tolerates a wide range of soils, including saline, acidic, alkaline and heavy clays. Fixes nitrogen.

Distribution: Originates in Central and South America and has been introduced in subtropical and tropical areas world-wide, including Burma, Thailand, Vietnam, Malaysia, Indonesia and the Philippines.

References: Hensleigh & Holaway (1988), Westphal & Jansen (1993).

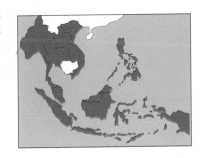

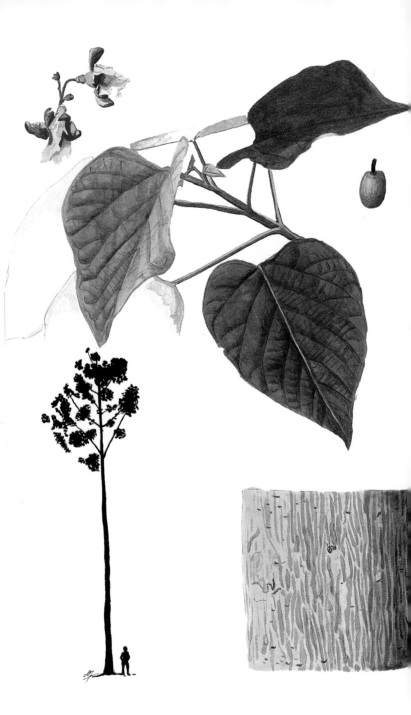

Key characteristics: Medium sized tree; thin grey bark; heart shaped, entire, opposite leaves, 10-20 cm long and 7-13 cm wide with waxy bloom below; trumpet shaped yellow to brown flowers.

Gmelina arborea

Verbenaceae

Common names: Yemane (trade name), gmelina, gumhar, malay beechwood (En); yemani, mai saw (Bur); so, so-maeo (Tha).

Description: A medium sized tree up to 40 m tall and 140 cm in diameter, but usually smaller than this. Bark is thin and grey. Leaves are opposite, more or less heart-shaped, 10-25 cm x 5-18 cm, smooth or velvety beneath. The yellow or brown flowers are arranged in panicled cymes, 15-30 cm long, and appears after leaf-fall. The trumpet-shaped flowers are 4 cm long, nodding, hairy and short stalked. The fruits are ovate or pyriform, 2-2.5 cm long and contain 1-4 seeds.

Use: The wood is used for light construction and pulp as well as fuelwood and charcoal, and the leaves are good cattle fodder. A number of plant parts have medicinal value.

Ecology: Found in rain forests as well as dry deciduous forests. Tolerates a wide range of conditions from sea level to 1,200 m altitude and annual rainfall from 750-5,000 mm. Prefers temperatures between 21-28°C and moist fertile soils.

Distribution: Originates in an area from Pakistan and Sri Lanka to Burma, but is now widely planted in S.E. Asian countries, including Burma, Thailand, southern China, Vietnam, Indonesia and the Philippines.

References: Soerianegara & Lemmens (1994), Hensleigh & Holaway (1988), Little (undated).

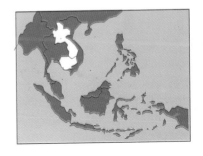

Key characteristics: Shrub or small tree; branches in whorls down to base of trunk; leaves opposite, with bent and joining secondary nerves; flowers in whorls at nodes. Fruit nutlike, yellow to red or purple, with one seed.

Trees and Fruits of Southeast Asia

Gnetum gnemon

Synonyms: *Gnetum acutatum*, *G. vinosum*

Common names: *G. gnemon* var. *gnemon*: Melinjo, Spanish joint fir (En); voë khlaèt (Cam); melinjo, belinjo, bagoe (Ins); meninjau, belinjau (Mal); hyinbyin, tanyin-ywe (Bur); bago, banago (Phi); peesae (Tha); gam cay, bét (Vie). *G. gnemon* var *tenerum*: phak miang, phak kariang, liang (Tha).

Description: A slender evergreen tree, 5-10 m tall, branching in whorls from the base. Trunk straight, with conspicuous, raised rings and grey bark. Branches thickened at base. Leaves opposite, elliptical, 7.5-20 cm long and 2.5-10 cm wide with secondary nerves bent and joining. The 3-6 cm long flowerstands are axillary, also from the older wood with flowers in whorls at the nodes. Female flowers 5-8 at each node, globose and tipped. The nut-like, ellipsoid fruit is 1-3.5 cm long, shortly apiculate first yellow then red to purple when ripe, containing one seed. Cultivated trees, belonging to *G. gnemon* var. *gnemon*, are larger in trée size and fruits. Other varieties, including *G. gnemon* var. *tenerum*, are shrub-like with much smaller fruits.

Use: The young leaves, inflorescence and fruits are cooked in vegetable dishes. The seed can be eaten raw, but is usually cooked or preserved as pounded flat cakes from which crispy snacks can be made. The bark provides a high quality fibre used for fishing lines and nets (it is durable in sea water).

Ecology: Found in rain forests up to 1,200 m altitude, commonly on riverbanks. For cultivation areas with a distinct dry season is preferable in order to synchronize fruiting. Apparently no specific requirements to soil, although moisture must be available during the dry season.

Distribution: Found and cultivated throughout Southeast Asia.

References: Verheij & Coronel (1992).

Key characteristics: Evergreen; straight bole; cone shaped crown; new twigs and branchlets with grey or rust colored hairs; leaves fernlike, silky white haired below; flowers 4-merous yellow.

Trees and Fruits of Southeast Asia

Grevillea robusta   Proteaceae

Common names: Silky oak, grevillea (En); khadaw hmi (Bur); son india (Tha); cây trài-bàn (Vie).

Description: A small to medium sized evergreen tree up to 20 m tall (sometimes higher) with a straight bole up to 90 cm in diameter and cone-shaped crown. Bark on young trees grey and smooth, on older trees deeply fissured, grey-black with oblong scales. New twigs and branchlets covered with grey or rust colored hairs. Leaves are alternate, fernlike, 15-30 cm long divided into (9-21) pairs of leaflets, each 4-9 cm long, with deep narrow lobes, dark shiny green and hairless above, silky white haired below. The inflorescence is 7.5 to 18 cm long racemes borne on the trunk, leafless parts of twigs and at leaf bases with showy yellowish flowers with 4 narrow sepals 12 mm long, crowded on one side of inflorescence axis. The podlike flattened fruits are 2 cm long, black with long slender stalks and 1-2 seeds inside.

Use: Used for timber and fuelwood and planted as an ornamental and shade tree. A gum can be extracted from the trunk. The flower provides a basis for honey production.

Ecology: Grows naturally in subtropical areas.

Distribution: From its origin in eastern Australia, it has been widely introduced to tropical and subtropical areas worldwide, including Burma, Thailand and Vietnam.

References: F/FRED (1992), Little (Undated).

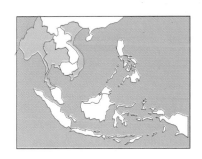

Key characteristics: Medium sized tree; straight stem; trifoliate leaves of variable size, leaflets elliptic or obovate; fruits 3-lobed capsules, 3-5 cm in diameter; white latex in all parts.

Hevea brasiliensis
Euphorbiaceae

Common names: Para rubber, natural rubber (En); kausuu (Cam); karet (Ins); jaang (Lao); getah asli (Mal); kyetpaung kaw bat (Bur); yang phara (Tha); cây cao su (Vie).

Description: A quick-growing tree up to 25m tall (wild trees may reach 40 m) with copious white to yellow latex in all parts. Leaves spirally arranged, trifoliate with nectaries at junction of leaflet and the 2-70cm long leaf stalk (normally about 15 cm). Leaflets are short stalked, elliptic or obovate, entire, 4-50 x 1.5-15cm, with acute base and pointed tip, dark green and smooth above, paler below. About 20 pairs of veins are pinnate. Leaves may be shed completely or partly during dry periods. Numerous small flowers are borne in soft-haired panicles with few female and numerous male flowers separated. Female flowers are 8mm long with yellow, bell-shaped calyx, with 5 triangular lobes and no petals. Male flowers 5 mm long with 10 anthers in two circles.

Use: The main use is the latex (rubber) from which directly or indirectly about 50,000 different products are produced. Its importance receded somewhat after the emergence of synthetic rubber. The wood has become popular for furniture making. Traditionally seeds were eaten after boiling to remove their poisonous contents.

Ecology: Wild rubber grows in evergreen tropical rain forest, often in periodically flooded areas, where climate is hot, humid and shows little seasonal variation. Some drought is tolerated, though. Although the tolerable pH range is quite wide (pH 4-8), it prefers deep well drained loams of pH 5-6. Lime is not tolerated.

Distribution: Originates in tropical South America. Now also grown in Burma, Thailand, China, Cambodia, Vietnam, Malaysia, Indonesia and southern Philippines.

References: Purseglove (1974), Westphal & Jansen (1993).

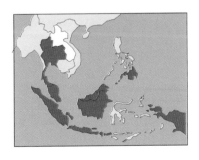

Key characteristics: Large; some-times buttressed; bark grey with orange tinge; leaves with 2 pairs of leaflets; flowers white and pink with only one petal; freshly cut wood smells like beans.

Intsia bijuga

Leguminosae
(Caesalpinioideae)

Synonyms: *Macrolobium bijugum, Eperua decandra, Afzelia bijuga, Albizia bijuga*

Common names: Borneo teak, moluccan ironwood (En); merbau (Mal); tat-talum (Bur); praduu thale, lumpho thale (Tha).

Description: A broadly crowned large tree up to 45 m tall and 200 cm in diameter, sometimes buttressed. Deciduous in areas with dry season. Bark is grey tinged with orange. The leaves are alternate, compound with two (rarely three) pairs of opposite, papery leaflets, 8-12 cm x 5-8.5 cm, asymmetric ovate-obovate with round base and emarginate tip. Flowers are white and pink, clustered on terminal panicles (corymbs) and have only one white petal. Pods are 10-25 cm long and 4-6.5 cm wide and contains 1-8 dark brown seeds. Freshly cut wood smells like raw beans.

Use: A premium wood for posts, flooring, furniture, panelling, stairs, window and door frames. Dye can be extracted from wood and bark. Seeds and bark are used in traditional medicine.

Ecology: Tropical lowland tree growing scattered along seashores and swamps and sometimes stream banks in areas receiving 2,000 mm annual rain or more. Prefers sandy soils but tolerates a wide range of types. Nitrogen fixing.

Distribution: Native to Southeast Asia and Southwestern Pacific islands and found in Burma, Thailand, Cambodia, Vietnam, Malaysia and the Philippines.

References: Guzman et al (1986), Hensleigh & Holaway (1988).

Key characteristics: Medium sized tree; bark with thin yellowish lines; leaves mostly opposite, large, entire; large, purplish, showy flowers; seeds winged.

Lagerstroemia speciosa

Lythraceae

Synonym: *Lagerstroemia flos-reginae*

Common names: Queens flower (En); pyinma (Bur); banaba (Phi); chuang-muu, tabaek-dam, baa-ngo ba saa, inthanin (Tha); bàng-lang nuoc (Vie).

Description: Up to 30 m tall and 40 cm in diameter. Bark grey with thin yellowish lines. Leaves simple, opposite or slightly alternate, entire, usually smooth and rather large, becoming reddish or yellow before falling. Young leaves dull reddish brown and very shiny. The flowers are usually purplish, 2.5-3 cm long, grouped at tip of branches. The fruit is a small ovoid or ellipsoid capsule, 2-3.5 cm in diameter with small, pale brown seeds inside with 12-18 mm long wings.

Use: The wood is used for agricultural implements and the leaves have medicinal value. Often planted as an ornamental along city streets.

Ecology: Grows naturally in secondary forests at low to medium altitudes.

Distribution: Outside India common in Burma, Thailand, China, Vietnam, Malaysia and the Philippines.

References: Guzman et al (1986).

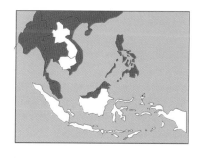

Key characteristics: Bole irregularly fluted; steep buttresses;
furrowed bark mottled grey and orange and with milky, sticky
sap; twigs and leaves sometimes hairy; leaves odd-pinnate with
6-9 leaflets; fruit up to 5 cm in diameter, yellowish hairy.

Lansium domesticum · Meliaceae

Synonyms: *Aglaia dookoo, A. domestica, A. aquea*

Common names: Langsat (En); langsat, duku, kokosan (Ins, Mal); langsat, duku (Bur); lansones, buahan (Phi); langsat, duku, longkong (Tha); bòn-bon (Vie).

Description: Tree, up to 30 m high and 75 cm in diameter (in cultivation 5-10 m tall). Bole irregularly fluted, with steep buttresses and furrowed bark, mottled grey and orange and containing milky, sticky sap. Twigs sometimes hairy. Leaves alternate, odd-pinnate, 30-50 cm long with 6-9 leaflets, smooth to densely haired with leaf stalk up to 7 cm long. Leaflets alternate, elliptical to oblong, 9-21 cm long and 5-10 cm wide, glossy, paper-like to leathery with asymmetrical base, shortly pointed tip and 10-14 pairs of lateral veins. Stalks of leaflets 5-12 mm long, thickened at base. Inflorescence many-flowered 10-30 cm long raceme, single or in groups of 2-10 on trunk or large branches. Flowers small with fleshy, cup-shaped, greenish-yellow calyx with 5 lobes. Petals fleshy, white to pale yellow, 2-3 x 4-5 mm. Fruit an ellipsoid or globose berry, 2-4 x 1.5-5 cm (or larger), yellowish hairy with persistent calyx, thin skin and white translucent flesh.

Use: Fruit eaten fresh. Tough and durable wood for house posts, tool handles and similar. Dried fruit peels are burnt as a mosquito repellant. Fruit peel, seeds and barks have various traditional medicinal uses.

Ecology: Grows in sheltered, shaded and humid environments up to 800m altitude, with well distributed rainfall and preferably well drained, humus rich and slightly acid soil.

Distribution: Native to western Southeast Asia from Thailand through Malaysia and Indonesia to the Philippines. Small scale cultivation in Burma and Vietnam.

References: Verheij & Coronel (1992).

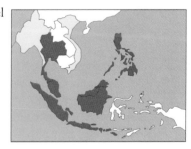

Key characteristics: Bipinnately compound leaves with 10-20 pairs of leaflets on each pinnae; flowers white, in round heads 2-2.5 cm in diameter; "giant" forms are distinguished from *L. diversifolia* by two, 1-2 mm wide round glands on the leaf stalk at the first and last pair of pinnae of most leaves.

Leucaena leucocephala

Leguminosae
(Mimosoideae)

Synonyms: *Leucaena glauca*, *L. latisiliqua*

Common names: Leucaena (En), kânthum theet, kratin (Cam); lomtoro (Ins, Mal); kan thin (Lao); ipil-ipil (Phi); kra thin (Tha); bo chét, schemu (Vie).

Description: Several types exists from shrubs to small or medium sized trees. "Giant" types may reach 20 m in height. Bark is smooth, grey to brown with small tan spots. Leaves alternate, evenly bipinnate and 10-20 cm long with 4-10 cm long pinnae. Each pinnae has 10-20 pairs of oblong or lanceolate leaflets, 8-15 mm long and 3 mm wide, that folds up in the night. Leaf base is sub-equal or oblique. The yellowish-white flowers are grouped in round flower heads 2-2.5 cm in diameter. Pods are 10-20 cm long and 1.5 to 2 cm wide, flat and pointed in both ends, brown when ripe.

Use: Reforestation, erosion control and soil improvement. Wood used for light construction, poles, pit props, pulp, furniture, flooring and fuelwood. Green parts are used as fodder and green manure.

Ecology: As a tropical lowland pioneer species it is fast growing, competitive and thrives in full sunlight and survives with little water. However, it grows best with 1,000-3,000 mm evenly distributed annual rain, neutral to alkaline soils and temperatures between 22-30°C. Although some provenances are adapted to higher elevations, most forms thrive better below 500 m elevation. A major setback for the use of this species has been the widespread infestation by psyllids.

Distribution: Native to South Mexico and the northern part of Central America. It has been introduced throughout the tropics and has become naturalized in many places, including most countries in Southeast Asia, but not from Laos.

References: F/FRED (1992), Hensleigh & Holaway (1988), MacDicken (1994), Westphal & Jansen (93).

Key characteristics: Short stocky trunk; often broad crown; compound leaves with 2-5 pairs of oblong-lanceolate leaflets; yellow-white flowers, red to purple, round fruits, about 3 cm in diameter, with flat warts.

Litchi chinensis   Sapindaceae

Synonyms: ssp. chinensis: *Dimocarpus litchi, Litchi sinense, Nephelium litchi*; ssp. philippinensis: *Euphoria didyma, Lichi philippinensis*; ssp. javanensis: *L. chinensis f. glomeriflora*

Common names: ssp. chinensis: Lychee, litchi (En); kuléén (Cam); litsi, klèngkeng, kalèngkeng (Ins); ngèèw (Lao); laici, kelengkang (Mal); kyet-mouk, lin chi, lam yai (Bur); linchee, litchi, see raaman (Tha); vai, cay vai, tu hú (Vie).

Description: A medium sized, long lived tree, up to 30 m high with a short stocky trunk, and often crooked and twisted branches forming a crown broader than height. Leaves are alternate, pinnately compound of 2-5 pairs of leaflets with 3-8 mm long petiolules. Leaflets are oblong-lanceolate, 3-16 cm long and 1.8-4 cm wide, paper like to leathery, deep green and glossy above, glaucous below. Inflorescences are well branched panicles, 5-30 cm long with many small, yellowish-white flowers with 4-merous calyx with 6-10 stamens. The fruits are round, 3-3.5 cm in diameter with thin leathery skin, bright red to purplish, usually with dense flat warts.

Use: Cultivated primarily for its fruit. Also provide the basis for excellent quality honey. The timber is very durable.

Ecology: Native to tropical and warm subtropical areas with short, dry and cool but frost free winters and long hot summers with annual rainfall above 1,200 mm and protection from wind. Quite exacting in these climatic requirements and usually do not flower elsewhere.

Distribution: Originates somewhere in the area between southern China, northern Vietnam and Malaysia. Now also found in cool highlands in Thailand and Bali, Indonesia.

References: Verheij & Coronel (1992).

Key characteristics: Spreading crown; leaves in whorls of 3, leathery, long and narrow with irregularly spiny-toothed, undulating margin when young; flowers creamy white; fruit is a nut.

Macadamia integrifolia

Proteaceae

Synonym: *Macadamia ternifolia* var. *integrifolia*

Common name: Macademia nut (En).

Description: A tree up to 18 m tall with a largely spreading crown up to 15 m in diameter. The oblong to lanceolate, leathery leaves, occurring in whorls of 3, are 10-30 cm long and 2-4 cm wide, irregularly spiny-dentate when young, later with entire margin. Leaf stalks 5-15 mm long. The inflorescence is raceme borne in leaf corners (axillary), 10-30 cm long, bearing 100-500 creamy white flowers in groups of 2-4, each about 12 mm long, with 4 sepals. Fruit globose, 2.5-4 cm in diameter with one seed (nut) inside.

Use: The nut is of very high quality and is the primary product of this tree. The decomposed husk is used in potting soils.

Ecology: The macadamia nut grows naturally in the fringe of subtropical rain forests and tolerates quite harsh conditions

Distribution: Native to rainforests of Queensland and New South Wales in Australia. After its successful introduction into Hawaii, trees have been planted in several Southeast Asian countries, particularly in Thailand.

References: Verheij & Coronel (1992).

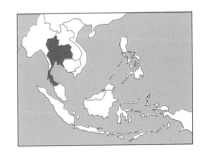

Mangifera altissima

Mangifera
foetida

M. altissima
Key characteristics: Prominent leaf scars, midrib &
nerves; panicles 10-25 cm
long; 4-merous flowers; fruit
8 x 6 cm, yellow when ripe.

M. foetida
Key characteristics: Straight
trunk; irritant whitish sap in
bark; leaf stalk very swollen;
flowers reddish-pink, 5-
merous; fruit to 14 x 12 cm,
thick skin.

Trees and Fruits of Southeast Asia

Mangifera altissima

Anacardiaceae

Synonyms: *Mangifera rumphii*, *M. merrilli*, *Buchanania reticulata*

Common names: Medang kok, membacang (Ins); paho, pahutan, pangamangaen (Phi).

Description: Erect, 12-35m tall and 35-80cm in diameter. Branchlets angular. Leaves elliptic to oblong-lanceolate, 15-43cm long, 2-11cm wide, smooth, papery, dark green above, cuneate base, entire margin, pointed tip. Midrib and nerves prominent, veins reticulate, leaf stalk 1.5-9cm long. Prominent leaf scars. Flowers at tip of twigs or from leaf corners, crowded towards the tip, panicles 10-25cm long, smooth, with small white or creamy-white flowers. Calyx 4-lobed. 4 petals and 5 stamens. Fruit ellipsoid to ovoid, 5-8 x 3-6cm and about 40g, yellowish when ripe. Flesh white, slightly fibrous, acid to slightly sweet.

Use: The immature fruit can be eaten fresh, pickled or mixed with vegetables.

Ecology: Growing in lowland primary forest, up to 400 m altitude.

Distribution: Native to the Pacific, eastern Indonesia and the Philippines.

Mangifera foetida

Synonym: *Mangifera horsfeldii*.

Common names: Horse mango (En); svaay.sââ (Cam); bachang, limus, asem hambawang (Ins); bachang, machang, pahu (Mal); thayet-poh, lamut (Bur); xoài hôi (Vie).

Description: To 35m high. Straight trunk. Bark light-brown to dark grey-brown, shallowly fissured with broad, flat ridges. Irritant whitish sap becoming black on exposure. Crown dense, branches massive. Leaves elliptic-oblong to broadly elliptic or oblanceolate, 15-40cm x 9-15cm, stiff leathery, dark-green above, clear green below. Leaf stalk 1.5-8cm, stout and very swollen at base. Flowers in 10-40cm long, upright panicles near branch tips, small, reddish-pink, 5-merous, scentless. Fruit obliquely ovoid-oblong to globose, 9-14cm x 7-12cm, dirty dark olive-green to yellowish green with brown lenticels. Skin about 5 mm thick. Flesh pale orange to yellow, fibrous, juicy, strong turpentine smell. Stone fibrous, about 6 x 5 x 3cm.

Use: Not highly valued, but mature fruit eaten fresh,. Younger fruits contains irritant juice and must be washed in salted water before used in fruit salads or pickle. Wood used for light indoor construction. Leaves and seeds are used in traditional medicine.

Ecology: Mainly in lowland rainforest areas with abundant and evenly distributed rainfall.

Distribution: Native to Thailand, Malaysia and Indonesia and introduced to southern Burma, Cambodia and Vietnam. In other S.E Asian countries rarely cultivated.

References: Verheij & Coronel (1992).

Key characteristics: Medium to large tree; short trunk; big crown; leaves spirally arranged, narrow elliptic to lanceolate, to 40 cm long, undulate margin; leaf stalk swollen; flowers green-yellow, 5-merous; fruit to 30 x 10 cm.

Mangifera indica

Anacardiaceae

Common names: Mango (En); svaay (Cam); mangga, mempelam, ampelam (Ins, Mal); mwàngx (Lao); tharyetthi (Bur); mangga, paho, mango (Phi); xoài (Vie).

Description: An evergreen tree, 10-45 m high and 60-120 cm in diameter. Bark grey-brown with longitudinal fissures. Leaves produced in flushes, spirally arranged, simple, reddish when young, turning dark shiny green. Leaf stalk up to 10 cm long, swollen at base. Adult leaves from 8-40 cm long and 2-10 cm wide, usually narrowly elliptic to lanceolate, somewhat leathery with tapering base, pointed tip, often undulating margin and 12-30 pairs of nerves. Inflorescences widely branched panicles up to 60 cm long, at tip of branches, soft haired with yellow-green male and hermaphrodite flowers, 5-8 mm in diameter with 5-lobed calyx and 5 petals. Fruit a fleshy drupe, variable in size, shape and color, usually obovoid-oblongoid, unequal sided, up to 10cm x 30cm. Flesh yellow to orange, juicy and sweet to turpentine flavoured with a large flat seed inside.

Use: The fruit can, depending on the cultivar, be eaten unripe green, ripe or processed into pickles, chutney, dried slices, juice or canned in syrup. Seed kernels can be used as cattle and poultry feed. The wood is fairly strong and can be used for construction and other purposes and also makes excellent charcoal and is used as a substrate for mushroom growing.

Ecology: Grows in tropical and subtropical areas up to 1,200 m altitude if no frosts occur, but optimal temperature is 27°C. Rainfall between 350-2,500 mm is needed and a dry season facilitates fruit production.

Distribution: Probably originated in Indo-Burma region, but has been cultivated for several thousand years throughout Asia.

References: Hensleigh & Holaway (1988), Verheij & Coronel (1992).

Key characteristics: Bole often low branched and gnarled; inner bark pinkish or reddish; leaves silky white underneath.

Manilkara kaukii

Sapotaceae

Synonym: *Minusops kaukii*

Common names: Sawo kecik, kayu sawo, sabo (Ins); sawah, sawai, sawau (Mal); lamut-thai, lamut-sida (Tha); gang-néo (Vie).

Description: A medium sized tree up to 25 m high and 100 cm in diameter, often with a low-branched and gnarled bole. Bark greyish-brown to dark brown, cracked to deeply fissured with pinkish or reddish inner bark. Leaves spirally arranged, clustered towards tip of twigs, simple, entire, leathery, usually obovate with rounded tip, parallel secondary and tertiary veins, silky white underneath. Inflorescences in corners of leaves or leaf scars, 1-many flowered, usually with hermaphroditic flowers. Flower buds are ovoid, flower stalks not thickened, calyx up to 7 mm long. The fruit is ovoid or obovoid and up to 3.7 cm long.

Use: Timber is used for construction and especially for furniture and carving. Fruits are edible. This species is also used as a rootstock for *Manilkara zapota*.

Ecology: Mostly growing in coastal, fairly dry areas, up to about 500 m altitude.

Distribution: Found in Burma, Thailand, Cambodia, Vietnam, Peninsular Malaysia, throughout Indonesia (except Kalimantan), Papua New Guinea and northeast Australia.

References: Soerianegara & Lemmens (1994).

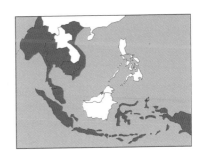

Key characteristics: Rich in white latex; low branched; rough
dark brown bark; oblong to lanceolate leaves with numerous
parallel nerves; flowers brown hairy outside, fruit reddish to
yellow-brown with brown scurf.

Manilkara zapota

Sapotaceae

Synonyms: *Achras zapota*, *Pouteria mammosa*, *Nispero achras*, *Manilkara achras*.

Common names: Sapodilla, noseberry (En); lomut (Cam); sawo manila, ciku, sawo londo (Ins); lamud (Lao); ciku (Mal); chico (Phi); lamut, lamut-farang (Tha); xabôchê, hông xiêm, tam lu'c (Vie).

Description: An evergreen upright tree, usually up to 20 m tall but occasionally reaching 30 m. A low branched trunk with rough dark brown bark and pyramid-shaped to globose crown. Leaves are alternate, ovate-elliptic to oblong-lanceolate, 3.5-15 cm long and 1.5-7 cm wide, cuneate or obtusely pointed at both ends, often emarginate, entire, smooth, glossy dark green with prominent midrib below and numerous parallel, lateral nerves. Leaf stalk 1-3.5 cm long. White, 6-merous flowers single on 1-2 cm long flower stalk in upper leaf corners, up to 1.5 cm in diameter, brown hairy outside. The fruit is a globose, ovoid or ellipsoid berry, 3-8 x 3-6 cm with dull reddish to yellow-brown thin skin, covered with sandy brown scurf. Flesh juicy, soft, yellow to red-brown, sweet with 0-12 oblong, 2 cm long brown or black seeds inside. All plant parts rich in white latex.

Use: Fruit eaten fresh or used in sherbets, ice cream, butter, jam or syrup. Latex previously used as basis for chewing gum and many industrial applications. Wood excellent for furniture. Seeds, flowers and bark tannin have medicinal uses.

Ecology: Adaptable species, found up to 2,500 m altitude. Survives light frost, long drought, strong winds and salt spray. However, does best at lower altitudes on rich, well drained sandy loams. Tolerates most soils including very saline.

Distribution: Originates in Central America, Mexico and West Indies. Now widespread all over Southeast Asia.

References: Hensleigh & Holaway (1988), Verheij & Coronel (1992).

Key characteristics: Shrub or small tree; umbrella-shaped crown; bark corky or gummy; deciduous; oddly bi- or tri-pinnate leaves 20-70 cm long; leaflets ovate, 1-2 cm long, whitish below; seed pods 15-45 cm long, with 9 ribs and 3 valves; white fragrant flowers.

Moringa oleifera

Moringaceae

Synonyms: *Moringa pterygosperma*, *M. moringa*

Common names: Horse raddish tree, drumstick tree, ben oil tree (En); dan-da-lun (Bur); malungai (Phi); ma-rum (Tha); chùm ngây (Vie).

Description: A fast growing deciduous shrub or small tree up to 12 m tall and 30 cm in diameter with an umbrella-shaped open crown (unless repeatedly coppiced). The bark is corky and gummy. Leaves are alternate, oddly bi- or tri-pinnately compound, triangular in outline and 20-70 cm long. Each pinnae has 3-9 pairs of 1-2 cm long ovate leaflets, soft dark green above and whitish below. The white, fragrant flowers are in pendulous panicles 1.5-2 cm long from leaf corners. The fruit pods are 15-45 cm long, 9-ribbed capsules opening by three valves to release the 3-winged seeds.

Use: Although the wood is soft, it is often used for firewood. The leaves are commonly eaten as a vegetable or used as livestock fodder. Flowers are cooked in soups. Pods are edible when young and oil is extracted from the seeds. The root can be eaten as a substitute for horse raddish. Also produces good quality honey. Roots, bark, leaves and oil are used in traditional medicine.

Ecology: Tropical pioneer species along watercourses, ponds and lakes, up to 750 m altitude, in areas with annual rainfall of 750-2,250 mm. Adaptable to soil conditions but does not tolerate water-logging.

Distribution: Originates in India and Arabia but is now naturalized throughout the tropics. Not reported from Cambodia.

References: Hensleigh & Holaway (1992).

Key characteristics: Small; branching from base; leaves ovate, serrate, sometimes lobed; flowers small, white; fruits red, white or purple; heavily pruned in cultivation.

Morus alba   Moraceae

Common names: Mulberry (En); posa (Bur); mon (Tha); dâu-tàm (Vie).

Description: A shrub or small tree up to 12 m tall, branching from the base. Bark smooth and light in color when young, becoming darker and fissured by age. Leaves ovate, serrate, occasionally deeply lobed, 5-7 cm long. Flowers are small and white, male and female flowers on seperate stalks. Fruit 2.5-5 cm long, consisting of many small drupes, red, white or purple in color, sweet and juicy. In cultivation the mulberry tree is usually heavily pruned and remains small, shrubby or hedge-like.

Use: Leaves provides the main source of food for silk worms and can also be fed to rabbits, swine and cattle. The berries can be eaten fresh or made into jellies and jams. Bark has traditionally been used for paper production in China and Nepal. Wood is used for fuel and sports goods like tennis rackets and hockey sticks.

Ecology: Prefers slightly acid, deep soils, in areas where annual mean temperatures are within the range of 12 to 29°C and annual rainfall from 600 to 1,400 mm. In the Himalayas found up to 2,000 m altitude.

Distribution: Originates in China and is now found in many Southeast Asian countries including Burma, Thailand and Vietnam.

References: F/FRED (1992), Purseglove (1974).

Key characteristics: Small, evergreen tree; soft haired branches spreading like a fan; leaves simple, serrate, grey haired below; 5-merous white flowers; fruit a red berry, 15 mm in diameter.

Muntingia calabura
Flacourtiaceae

Common names: Capulin, Jamaica cherry (En); krakhôb barang (Cam); cerri, kersen, talok (Ins); kerukup siam (Mal); hnget-thagya (Bur); datiles (Phi); takhop farang, krop farang (Tha); trúng ca, mat sam (Vie).

Description: A small evergreen tree up to 12 m high, growing and flowering continuously with soft haired, hanging branches spreading horizontally like a fan. Leaves alternate, simple, ovate-lanceolate, 4-14 cm long and 1-4 cm wide with serrated margin and grey hairy lower leaf surface. The 5-merous, white flowers borne in 1-5-flowered groups. Fruit a dull red berry, 15 mm in diameter with thousands of tiny seeds in soft flesh.

Use: The sweet berries can be eaten fresh or made into jam. The bark can be made into ropes and the flowers are used in traditional medicine.

Ecology: Typical pioneer species on disturbed sites in tropical lowlands up to 1,000 m altitude, preferably on slightly acid soil.

Distribution: Although not native to Southeast Asia and usually not actually cultivated, it has become one of the most common roadside trees in the region after its initial introduction to the Philippines.

References: Hensleigh & Holaway (1988), Verheij & Coronel (1992).

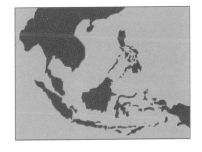

Key characteristics: Small; branchlets slender; leaves elliptic or oblong-lanceolate, 8-11 pairs of lateral veins, aromatic; Male and female flowers mostly on seperate trees, pale yellow; fruit broad pyriform drupe splitting into two halves, seed dark brown, aril red.

Myristica fragrans   Myristicaceae

Common names: Nutmeg (En); pala banda, bunga pala (Ins); chan theed (Lao); buah pala, bunga pala (Mal); zadeik-po (Bur); chan thet (Tha); dâu khâu (Vie).

Description: An evergreen tree up to 5-13 m tall, reaching sometimes 20 m, with slender branches and superficial roots. Crown conical if free standing. Alternate leaves on about 1 cm long leaf stalks, elliptic or oblong-lanceolate, acute base and pointed tip, dark shiny green above and paler beneath, 5-15 cm long and 2-7 cm wide with 8-11 pairs of lateral veins and aromatic smell when crushed. Male and female flowers mostly on separate trees in similar looking umbels arising from leaf corners, 1-10 flowers, about 5-7 mm long, in male cymes and 1-3, about 1 cm long flowers in female, on 1-1.5 cm long stalks. Waxy, fleshy flowers fragrant, pale yellow and glabrous with bell-shaped calyx and no petals. Fruit a smooth, fleshy, yellow drupe, 6-9 cm long with longitudinal ridge, splitting in two when ripe, exposing purplish-brown shiny seed in a red aril.

Use: Two spices can be produced from M. fragrans: nutmeg from the dried seed and mace from the dried aril. Essential oils can be extracted from the seeds.

Ecology: In its native Molucca nutmegs are grown on rich volcanic soils up to 500 m altitude in a non-seasonal climate of 2,200-3,600 mm annual rain and temperatures from 24 to 33°C. Prefers some shade when young and does not tolerate waterlogging or excessive soil drying. Very rarely found growing wild.

Distribution: Originates in the Molucca Islands from where it has, more or less successfully, been introduced into Thailand, Malaysia, Singapore, elsewhere in Indonesia and outside the region.

References: Purseglove (1974), Westphal & Jansen (1993).

Key characteristics: Alternate, jugate leaves, hairy below; flowers white, yellowish greenish, no petals; fruit reddish with dense curved hair-like appendages.

Nephelium lappaceum

Sapindaceae

Synonyms: *Nephelium glabrum*, *N. chryseum*, *N. sufferugineum*

Common names: Rambutan (En); saaw maaw, ser mon (Cam); rambutan (Ins, Mal,Phi); usan (Phi); ngoh, phruan (Tha); chôm chôm, vai thiêù (Vie).

Description: A fairly large tree in natural vegetation, but cultivated trees are about 4-7 m high with spreading crown. Leaves are alternate, jugate with up to 6 pairs of, ovate to obovate leaflets, 5-28 cm long and 2-10.5cm wide, smooth above, sometimes hairy on midrib, below variably hairy, nerves slightly to strongly curving. Inflorescence axillary, superficially appearing to be at branch tips. Flowers white, yellowish or greenish with 4-5 (sometimes 7) sepals, about 1-2 mm long and no petals. Trees with male or hermaphroditic flowers, the latter being functionally either male or female. The fruit ellipsoid or sub-globular, up to 5 x 7 cm or 20-95 g, yellow to purplish-red with dense, filiform, curved, 0.5-2 cm long appendages.

Use: Sweet fruits are eaten fresh, sour ones can be stewed first. Can also be canned or made into jam although losing some of its taste. Leaves, bark, fruit, roots all have various traditional medicinal uses. Young shoots are used for silk dye and a solid fat can be produced from the seed kernel.

Ecology: Low or middle-storey tree in primary and secondary forest types in humid tropical lowlands up to 600 m altitude, on dry to swampy weakly acid soils, with annual rainfall of 2,500 mm or more and low wind exposure.

Distribution: The origin is not known, but rambutan is now found from southern China through Thailand, Cambodia, Vietnam, Malaysia and Indonesia to the Philippines.

References: Verheij & Coronel (1992).

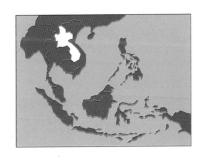

Key characteristics: Spreading flat crown; smooth bark with corky warts; bipinnate leaves, leaflets asymmetrical, 6-12 mm long, 3-5 mm wide; flowers white, fragrant; pods thin walled, 10-13 cm long.

Trees and Fruits of Southeast Asia

Paraserianthes falcataria   Leguminosae

Synonyms: *Albizia falcataria, A. falcata, A. moluccana, Adenanthera falcata, Adenanthera falcataria*

Common names: Molucca albizia, Indonesia albizia, white albizia (En); djeungdjing, sengon, sengon laut (Ins); batai, kayu macis (Mal); thinbaw-magyi (Bur).

Description: A fast growing medium sized deciduous tree up to 30 m tall and 80 cm in diameter with a spreading, flat crown (narrow in dense planting). Bark greyish white and smooth with corky warts. Leaves alternate, bipinnately compound, 22-30cm long with 10-12 pairs of pinnae. Each pinnae is 5-10 cm long with 15-20 pairs of 6-12 mm long and 3-5 mm wide asymmetrical pointed leaflets. The 10-12 mm long creamy white and fragrant flowers are borne in 20-25 cm long inflorescence. The flat, thin walled pods are 10-13 cm long and 2 cm wide, first green, then brown.

Use: The soft, light wood is used for pulp, particle board, packing cases, boxes, matches, chopsticks, veneer and light furniture and sometimes as fuelwood. It can be pruned for mulch for soil improvement. Also used as a shade tree in plantations of coffee, tea, cacao and banana.

Ecology: Grows in the warm, humid tropical zone where the dry season is short and rainfall evenly distributed, mostly on well drained soils; nitrogen fixing.

Distribution: Originates in Papua New Guinea, eastern Indonesia and the Solomon Islands, from where it has been introduced to Malaysia, western Indonesia, the Philippines, Burma and other southeast Asian countries.

References: Hensleigh & Holaway (1988), Little (Undated), MacDicken (1994).

Key characteristics: Hairy branchlets; leaves bipinnately compound; leaflets 5-9 mm, rounded tips, with pointed lobe at base;
flowers in pear-shaped hanging heads; large, strongly twisted
pods.

Parkia speciosa
Leguminosae

Synonyms: *Parkia roxburghii, P. javanica*

Common names: Petai (Ins); sato, to dan, to khao (Tha).

Description: A 15-35 m high tree up to 50-100 cm in diameter. Branchlets hairy. Bipinnate leaves on 2-6 cm long stalks with gland 0.7-1.5 cm above stalk base. 14-18 pairs of pinnae, 5-9 cm long, each with 31-38 pairs of opposite linear leaflets, 5-9 mm long and about 2 mm wide, with rounded tip and small pointed lobe or ear at base. The inflorescence is hanging, pear-shaped heads. Pods 35-45 cm long and 3-5 cm wide, usually strongly twisted.

Use: (Young) seeds eaten raw or cooked or may be pickled. The pods may also be fed to swine. Branches are used for fuelwood and main trunk provides good furniture wood.

Ecology: Tropical lowland tree growing in areas with 1,000-2,000 mm annual rainfall, mean annual temperature about 24°C and well drained loamy or clay-loam soils. Requires some shade when young. Nitrogen fixing.

Distribution: Burma, Thailand, Peninsular Malaysia, Indonesia.

References: F/FRED (1992), Smitinand & Larsen (1985).

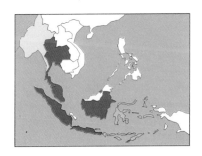

Key characteristics: Small to medium sized dome-shaped tree; spirally arranged leaves, simple, entire, with pleasant smell, reddish when young; flowers small, greenish, 3-merous; fruit large round or pyriform berry with green flesh.

Persea americana — Lauraceae

Synonym: *Persea gratissima*

Common names: Avocado, alligator pear (En); 'avôkaa (Cam); adpukat, avokad (Ins); avokado, apukado (Mal); htaw bat (Bur); awokado (Tha); bo', lê daù (Vie).

Description: A spreading dome-shaped tree up to 20 m tall, although normally about 8-10 m, with brittle twigs and often with drooping branches when older. Leaves alternate, simple and crowded at the shoot tips, with pleasant smell when crushed. The leaf blade is ovate, oblong, dark green and somewhat shiny above, dull below, 10-20 cm long and 3-10 cm wide. Flowers grouped in compound, soft haired panicles in the leaf corners and crowded towards the shoot tips. The small flowers are hermaphroditic, greenish cream colored and very fragrant. The large round, oblong, pear- or bottle-shaped fruits are 7-20 cm long and 7-10 cm wide, yellowish green to dark green, sometimes tinged with purple. Skin very variable: Shiny or dull, smooth or rough, thin and papery or thick and brittle or thick and leathery. One large seed, variable in shape, constituting about half the weight of the fruit. Avocado is divided into 3 races: Mexican, Guatemalan and West Indian.

Use: Grown primarily for its nutritious fruits, mainly eaten fresh. Oil extracts is used in cosmetic products. The fruit and leaves are used medicinally. Wood not durable but can provide lower quality firewood.

Ecology: A tropical and subtropical rain forest species. Mexican and Guatemalan races tolerate light frost. Tolerate a wide variety of well drained soils but not saline or waterlogged ones.

Distribution: Originates in Central America. Now growing in many tropical and subtropical areas of Southeast Asia.

References: Hensleigh & Haloway (1988), Purseglove (1974), Verheij & Coronel (1992).

Phyllanthus
emblica

Phyllanthus acidus

P. emblica
Key characteristics: Trunk often fluted/ twisted; foliage feathery; bark peeling off exposing orange-brown layer; leaves pinnately arranged, 7-25 mm long.

P. acidus
Key characteristics: Leaves ovate, 2-7cm long, pinnate; rosy, 4-merous flowers; yellow-white lobed fruit 1-2.5cm in diameter.

Phyllanthus acidus
Euphorbiaceae

Synonym: *Cicca acida*

Common names: Otaheite/malay gooseberry (En); ceremoi, cereme (Ins); chermai (Mal); thinbozihpyoo (Bur); iba, bangkiling, karmay (Phi); ma-yom (Tha); chùm ruôt (Vie).

Description: A shrub or small tree, 2-9m high. Leaves ovate, 2-7cm long, pinnately arranged along branches. Up to 12cm long panicles of rosy male, female or hermaphroditic, 4-merous flowers. Fruit roundish drupe, 1-1.3cm in diameter, yellow-white with 6-8 lobes and 4-6 seeds.

Use: Fresh acid fruits eaten raw with sugar, made into refreshing drink or cooked. Young leaves eaten as vegetable. Root bark used for tanning and the root has medicinal properties.

Ecology: Grows in tropical to subtropical moist areas, up to 1,000 m altitude.

Distribution: Probably from Madagascar. Now found all over Southeast Asia.

Phyllanthus emblica

Synonym: *Emblica officinalis*

Common names: Emblic, Malacca-tree, Indian gooseberry (En); melakka (Mal); makhaam pom (Tha).

Description: A small to medium sized, semi-deciduous tree up to 30m tall and 60cm in diameter. Trunk often fluted and twisted. Crown irregular with feathery pale green foliage. Bark thin, pale grey-brown, peeling off in oblong papery scales, exposing orange-brown layer. Twigs slender, reddish brown and fine haired. Leaves alternate in two rows, resembling pinnately compound leaf, 0.7-2.5cm long, 2-4mm wide with rounded base, pointed tip and slightly curved edges. Flowers tiny, short stalked, pale green to greenish yellow with 6 sepals and no petals. Male and female flowers usually on the same tree. Fruits rounded, smooth, almost stalkless, greenish yellow drupes, usually single near end of twig, 2-3cm (-5cm) in diameter, juicy and very sour.

Use: Fruits very rich in vitamin C. Eaten fresh, dried or pickled. Wood for excellent charcoal and firewood, and also used for posts, agricultural implements, furniture, low grade construction. Bark used for dyeing and tanning. Foliage used for livestock fodder and green manure.

Ecology: Grows on various soil types in dry and moist deciduous forests in tropical and subtropical areas with mild winters.

Distribution: Native to tropical Asia and found wild or cultivated in Burma, Thailand, southern China and Malaysia.

References: Little (Undated), National Research Council (1980), Verheij & Coronel (1992).

Key characteristics: Short trunk; crooked branches; bark grey and smooth; 4-10 mm long spines at leaf bases; leaves bipinnate with only one pair of leaflets; fruit pods curled up.

Pithecellobium dulce

Leguminosae
(Mimosoideae)

Synonyms: *Mimosa dulcis, Inga dulcis*; also spelled Pithecollobium or Pithecolobium

Common names: Guayamochil, Manila tamarind, sweet inga (En); am'pül tük (Cam); asam belanda, asem londo, asam koranji (Ins); khaam th'ééd (Lao); asam kranji, asam tjina (Mal); kway-tanyeng (Bur); makham-thet, makham-khong (Tha); me keo, keo tay (Vie).

Description: A semi-evergreen shrub or small tree up to 20 m high and 80-100 cm in diameter with short trunk, crooked branches and round glabrescent branchlets with 4-10 mm long spines at base of most leaves. Bark smooth, grey, becoming slightly rough and furrowed by age. Crown broad, up to 30 m in diameter. Leaves bipinnate with only one pair of pinnae, each with two ovate asymmetrical glabrous leaflets, 1.5-3.5 cm long and 1-2 cm wide. The up to 10 cm long inflorescence at end of branches, hairy with 15-20 whitish flowers in round heads each about 3-5 mm long. Fruit pods about 1 cm wide, somewhat flattened and curled up, reddish-brown. Seeds flat, black, surrounded by thick, spongy, dry "flesh".

Use: Fruit flesh is eaten fresh and the seed oil is also edible. Seeds can be used for animal feed. Tannin for softening leather is extracted from bark, seeds and leaves. The bark is used for dyeing fish nets. Leaves and root bark are used in traditional medicine. Although not the best quality the wood is used as fuel. The tree is also a good hedge plant and used as an avenue tree.

Ecology: Very tolerant tree that grow on a variety of soils at low to medium altitudes, at annual rainfall between 450 to 3,000 mm.

Distribution: Originating in Central America but now found in most southeast Asian countries including Burma, Thailand, Laos, Cambodia, Vietnam, Malaysia, Indonesia and the Philippines.

References: F/FRED (1992), Hensleigh & Holaway (1988), Little (Undated), Verheij & Coronel (1988).

Key characteristics: Low branching; green and red-brown bark, peeling off in flakes; young twigs hairy and quadrangular; leaves opposite, glandular.

Trees and Fruits of Southeast Asia

Psidium guajava

Myrtaceae

Synonym: *Psidium aromaticum*

Common names: Guava (En); jambu batu, biyabas (Bru); trapaek sruk (Cam); jambu biji, jambu klotok (Ins); sida (Lao); jambu biji, jambu kampuchia, jambu berase (Mal); Guava, bayabas, (Phi); malakapen (Bur); ma kuai, ma-man, farang (Tha); Oi (Vie).

Description: A shallow rooted shrub or small tree up to 10 m high, branching from the base. Bark green to red-brown, smooth and peeling off in flakes. Young twigs 4-angled and hairy. Leaves opposite, glandular, elliptical to oblong, 5-15 cm x 3-7 cm. Glabrous above and fine haired below. The white flowers are alone or a few together, about 3 cm in diameter with 4-5 petals. Fruit a globose berry, ovoid or pyriform, 4-12 cm long, very variable in size and flavour.

Use: The fruit is eaten fresh or used for preserves, jam, jelly or juice. Leaves can be used for dyeing and tanning and in traditional medicine (against diarrhea).

Ecology: Grows in tropical climates from sea level to about 1,600 m and adapts to a wide range of soil and climatic conditions. Seeds are easily spread naturally by birds.

Distribution: Indigenous to the American tropics, from where it was initially brought to the Philippines and India. Now common throughout most of the tropics, including all of Southeast Asia.

References: Purseglove (1974), Verheij & Coronel (1992).

Key Characteristics: Medium sized, to 2 m in diameter, more or less buttressed; bark with red sap; wood smell like camphor or cedar; wide spreading crown; lower branches drooping to ground; leaves oddly pinnate, 15-30 cm long; leaflets ovate, 5-10 cm; flowers yellow, 1.5 cm long, fragrant; seed pods circular with transparent wing around, 4-5.5 cm in diameter.

Pterocarpus indicus

Leguminosae
(Papilionoideae)

Synonyms: *Pterocarpus pallidus, P. blancoi, P. pubescens, P. wallichi, P. zollingen, P. papuanus*

Common names: Sono kembang (Ins); chan dêng (Lao); angsana (Mal); pashu-padauk (Bur); narra (Phi); duu baan, praduu baan (Tha).

Description: A medium sized deciduous tree up to 35 m tall and 2 m in diameter with fluted trunk and more or less pronounced buttresses, wide spreading crown with lower branches drooping and touching the ground. Bark smooth, light yellow-brown, 0.5 cm thick, exuding red sap when cut. The wood smell like camphor or cedar. Leaves oddly pinnate, 15-30 cm long with 7-11 alternate leaflets, each 5-10 cm, ovate to oblong ovate, blunt pointed and shiny, largest leaflets towards tip of leaf. The numerous yellow showy and fragrant flowers are 1.5 cm long, arranged in branched panicles. Seed pods are soft haired when young, becoming (almost) smooth when mature. Pods, including the 1-1.5 cm wide surrounding wing, are circular, flat, 4-5.5 cm in diameter and about 0.5 cm thick.

Use: The wood is used for furniture making, cabinets, decorative veneers and other specialty items and can also produce a red dye. The tree is also used as a shade tree for other crops and as an ornamental.

Ecology: Native habitat flat coastal plains behind mangrove swamps or along inland streams in primary and secondary forest where the dry season is not pronounced. Tolerates longer dry season but timber quality is reduced due to forking

Distribution: Widely distributed in Southeast Asia.

References: Hensleigh & Holaway (1988), Soerianegara & Lemmens (1994).

Key characteristics: Shrub or small tree; branching from base; each branch ends in a spine; sometimes spines on twigs; leaves mostly opposite.

Trees and Fruits of Southeast Asia

Punica granatum

Punicaceae

Common names: Pomegranate (En); totum (Cam); delima (Ins, Mal); phiilaa (Lao); salebin, talebin, thale (Bur); granada (Phi); thapthim (C.Tha); phila (N.E. Tha); bakoh (N.Tha); lu'u, thap lu'u (Vie).

Description: A deciduous shrub or small tree up to 6, sometimes 10 m in height. Often richly branching from the base, each branch ending in a spine. Often also spines from leaf corners. Leaves mostly opposite, sometimes sub-opposite or clustered, oblong-lanceolate, 1-9 cm long and 0.5-2.5 cm wide with acute or obtuse base, entire margin and obtuse or emarginate tip. Flowers 1-5 together at top of twigs, waxy, 4-5 cm long and wide with red to white petals. Fruits 6-12 cm in diameter, very variable in color, with leathery skin. The interior of the fruit is separated by membranous walls and white spongy tissue into compartments packed with numerous small transparent sacs filled with juicy pulp and seed.

Use: Fruit eaten fresh or made into juice or syrup. Almost every part of the plant have long traditions of medicinal use and ink can be prepared from the fruit rind.

Ecology: Hardy subtropical species tolerating low winter temperatures, drought and a wide range of soil conditions. In Southeast Asia found up to 1,600 m altitude. In areas with high rainfall evergreen with prolonged fruiting season but lower quality fruit.

Distribution: From its origin in central Asia, it has now spread to most subtropical and tropical countries, including all the countries covered by this field guide.

References: Verheij & Coronel (1992).

Key characteristics: Semi-deciduous, medium sized tree with milky latex; trifoliate leaves, red-yellow before falling off, hairy below; yellow-green 1cm long 5-merous flowers; globose golden-yellow hairy fruit, 5-8 cm in diameter with white flesh.

Sandoricum koetjape

Meliaceae

Synonyms: *Melia koetjape*, *Sandoricum indicum*, *S. nervosum*

Common names: Santol, kechapi, sentol (En); kôm piing riëch (Cam); kecapi, ketuat, sentul (Ins, Mal); toongz (Lao); thitto (Bur); kra thon, sa thon (Tha); sâú (Vie).

Description: A medium sized, semi-deciduous tree up to 30 m high and 90 cm in diameter with milky latex. Leaves alternate, trifoliate with a leaf stalk up to 18.5cm. Leaflets are elliptic to oblong-ovate, pointed at tip, shiny green above, pale green and fine haired below, top leaflet 6-26 cm x 3-16 cm, side leaflets 4-20 x 2-15cm, turning red-yellow before leaf fall. Flowers numerous, fragrant, yellowish-green, about 1 cm long with cup-shaped, 5 lobed calyx and 5 petals in 1 cm long. The fruit is a depressed globose, fine haired, golden yellow berry, most varieties 5-6 cm in diameter and 60-100 g, some cultivars from Thailand up to 7-9 cm and 300 g. Fruit flesh soft, white, sour to sweet with 2-5 glossy brown seeds.

Use: Fruits are eaten fresh or made into jams, jelly, marmalade, chutney or candy. Wood is used for construction, carpentry, household utensils and implements. Leaves, bark and roots have numerous medicinal uses.

Ecology: A hardy tree growing from lowland up to 1,000 m altitude, preferring well drained, clay loams or sandy clay loams with plenty of organic matter. Tolerates prolonged dry season but prefers more evenly distributed rainfall.

Distribution: Native to Indo-China and western Malesia and now cultivated or naturalized throughout tropical Asia, par-ticularly in Burma, Thailand, Vietnam, Malaysia, Indonesia and the Philippines.

References: Hensleigh & Holaway (1988), Verheij & Coronel (1992).

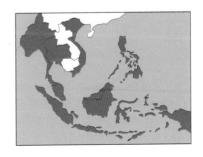

Key characteristics: Small tree; cylindrical trunk; bark grey, rough and furrowed; leaves smooth, pale green, evenly pinnate, 20-40 pairs of leaflets; flowers pink, cream or white; fruit pods 20-60 cm long, slightly curved.

Sesbania grandiflora

Leguminosae
(Papilionoideae)

Synonyms: *Agati grandiflora*, *Sesbania formosa*

Common names: Sesban (En); ture (Ins, Mal); paukpan-byu (Bur); katurai (Phi); khae, khae baan, khae daeng (Tha); so-dùa (Vie).

Description: A tree up to 12 m high with a cylindrical trunk up to 30 cm in diameter. Bark grey, rough and furrowed. The smooth leaves are alternate, evenly pinnate, 20-30 cm long with 20-40 pairs of oblong, obtuse, pale green leaflets, each 2.5-3.5 cm long. The 7-10 cm long and 3 cm wide flowers are cream colored or white. The fruits are 20-60 cm long pendula pods, 7-8 mm wide, slightly curved with 10-25 bean shaped seeds inside.

Use: Wood is used for low quality fuel and for paper pulp. Young leaves and green pods are eaten as a vegetable or used for livestock feed or green manure. Fresh flowers are used in stews and salads. The bark contains tanning agent, gum and fibers. Gum can also be produced from the seeds.

Ecology: Hardy lowland species adapted to difficult sites up to 800 m altitude on a wide range of soils, including waterlogged. Although it tolerates 6-7 months dry season, a shorter dry period and annual rain above 1,000 mm is preferable.

Distribution: Native to southern Asia and now found in most southeast Asian countries, including Burma, Thai-land, Vietnam, Malaysia, Indonesia and the Philippines.

References: Hensleigh & Holaway (1988).

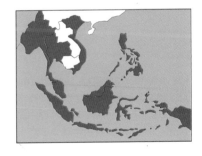

Key characteristics: Medium to large sized; sometimes buttresses; bark fissured, grey to reddish-brown; leaves with 4-
10 pairs of papery leaflets; flowers small, cream to white; fruit
bright orange, 4-10 x 3-8 cm.

Spondias cytherea   Anacardiaceae

Synonym: *Spondias dulcis*

Common names: Ambarella, otaheite apple, great hog plum (En); mokak (Cam); kedondong manis (Ins); kook hvaan (Lao); kedondong (Mal); gway (Bur); hevi (Phi); makok-farang (Tha); cóc (Vie).

Description: A quick growing large tree up to 45 m high and 90 cm in diameter, sometimes with buttresses. Bark shallowly fissured and greyish to reddish-brown. Leaves on 9-15 cm long stalks with 4-10 pairs of ovate-oblong to lanceolate, papery leaflets, each 5-25 cm long and 1.5-5 cm wide, with entire, serrate or crenate margin and pointed tip. Inflorescence, panicle at tips of branches up to 35 cm long, with small cream to white flowers, petals about 2.5 x 1 cm. The bright orange, ellipsoid or globose fruit is 4-10 cm long and 3-8 cm in diameter. Similar species: *Spondias purpurea* largely replaces this species in the Philippines. *S. purpurea* is distinguished by smaller leaflets (up to 5.5 cm long), smaller fruits (<4 cm) and red to purplish flowers.

Use: Fruit is eaten raw or stewed and used for jams, jellies and juice. The green fruit is used in salads, curries or in pickles. The fruits can be fed to pigs and the leaves to cattle. Steamed young leaves are also eaten as a vegetable. The wood is not of much use but leaves, bark and fruits are used in traditional medicine.

Ecology: Grows in the warm subtropics and the tropics up to about 700 m altitude and requires much light to fruit. Tolerates acid as well as limestone soils but the soil must be well drained. Tolerates drought and will primarily flower during the dry season when most leaves are shed. Where there is no pronounced dry season, flowering is continuous.

Distribution: Common in most of Southeast Asia except the Philippines where *S. purpurea* is more common.

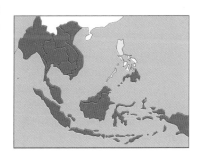

References: Verheij & Coronel (1992).

Swietenia
macrophylla

Swietenia
mahagoni

S. macrophylla
Key characteristics: Medium to large; high buttresses; inner bark red or pinkish-brown; 3-6 pairs of leaflets; flowers 5-merous; seed capsule brown, 10-22 cm long with 5 valves.

S. mahagoni
Key characteristics: Smaller tree; short, blunt buttresses; 2-5 pairs of leaflets; fruit capsule 4.5-10 cm long.

Swietenia macrophylla   Meliaceae

Synonyms: *Swietenia krukovii, S. belizensis*

Common names: Big-, broad- or large-leaved mahogany, Honduras mahogany (En); mahokkaanee bai yai (Tha); dái-ngua (Vie).

Description: A large tree up to 40-60 m high, branchless up to 18-25 m, and up to 200 cm in diameter, with buttresses up to 5 m high. Bark on older trees scaly, shaggy, deeply furrowed, brownish grey to reddish brown. Inner bark red-brown or pinkish red. Leaves alternate, even pinnate, with 2-8 pairs of leaflets, each about 9-13 x 3-4 cm. Flowerstands 10-20 cm long, flowers with 5-lobed calyx, ciliate sepals and 5 (or 4) petals. Light brown seed capsule, 10-22 cm long, opening by 5 valves, seeds 7.5-12 cm long, with wings.

Use: One of the finest timbers for high quality furniture and cabinet work, interior panelling, doors and decorative borders, boat building, musical instruments, carving and other uses. The bark is used for dying and tanning leather and oil can be extracted from the seed kernels. In India gum is tapped from cuts in the bark.

Ecology: Growing naturally in tropical rain forests up to 1,500 m altitude.

Distribution: From Central and South America. Planted throughout the tropics, including Burma, Thailand, Vietnam, Malaysia, Indonesia and the Philippines.

Swietenia mahagoni   Meliaceae

Common names: Small- or narrow-leaved mahogany, West Indian mahogany, Spanish or Cuban mahogany (En); mahokkaanee bai lek (Tha).

Description: To 30 m high, often with a short trunk and many branches. Buttresses short and blunt. Leaves alternate, 2-5 pairs of opposite leaflets, each 4-8 cm long and 1.5-3.3 cm wide. Inflorescence 5-18 cm long, flowers smooth. Fruit capsule 4.5-10 cm. Seeds 2-6 cm long.

Use and Ecology: As S. macrophylla.

Distribution: As S. macrophylla, except not reported from Vietnam.

References: Soerianegara and Lemmens (1994).

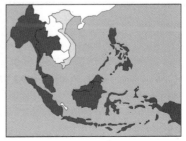

The map shows the distribution of both species.

Key characteristics: Trunk short, crooked, often branching from base; crown irregular; leaves opposite; flowers yellow-white; aqueum: 5-15 mm long leafstalk and 5-7mm long calyx, small fruits; samarangense: 3-5mm long leaf stalk, 15mm long calyx and larger fruit; aromatic.

Syzygium aqueum and S. samarangense

Myrtaceae

Synonyms: *Sysygium aqueum*: *Eugenia aquea, E. javanica, E. mindanaensis. S. samarangense*: *E. javanica, E. mananquil, Myrtus samarangensis, Jambosa alba*

Common names: Aqueum: Water apple, bell fruit (En); jambu air, jambu air mawar (Ins, Mal); tambis (Phi); machomphu-pa (Tha). Samarangense: Wax jambu, java apple (En); jambu semarang, jambu klampok (Ins); jambu air mawar (Mal); makopa (Phi); chomphu-kaemmaem, chomphu-khieo, chomphu-nak (Tha); man, roi (Vie).

Description: *S. aqueum*: 3-10m high with short crooked trunk, 30-50cm in diameter, often branching near base. Irregular crown. Leaves opposite, elliptic-cordate to obovate-oblong, 7-25cm long, 2.5-16cm wide, with 0.5-1.5cm long leaf stalk, sometimes with aromatic smell when crushed. Inflorescence at tip of twigs or from leaf axils with 3-7 yellow-white flowers, 2.5-3.5cm in diameter, calyx 5-7mm long, 4 petals about 7mm long. Fruit cone-shaped, glossy white to red, 1.5-2 cm long and 2.5-3.5 cm wide, watery with 1-2, sometimes 6 seeds. *E. samarangense* very similar but is somewhat larger, has thick, 3-5mm long leaf stalks, 15mm long calyx and larger pyriform fruits. Improved cultivars have green fruits. Leaves always aromatic smelling.

Use: Grown mainly for the fruit, which is eaten fresh, used in salads or sometimes pickled or stewed. The hard reddish wood can be used for construction, but the dimensions of *S. aqueum* are not very large. Various parts of *S. samarangense* are used in traditional medicine.

Ecology: Belongs to fairly moist tropical lowlands up to 1,200 m altitude, preferring heavy soils and easy access to water, also during the dry season, often planted along streams and ponds.

Distribution: Originates and widely distributed in Southeast Asia, including Burma, Thailand, Malaysia and Indonesia. In Vietnam listed as *Eugenia javanica* which is synonym for both species.

References: Guzman et al. (1986), Verheij & Coronel (1992).

Key characteristics: Low branching, irregular crown; bark rough, dark grey below, light and smooth above; leaves opposite, pinkish when young, faint turpentine smell if crushed; 4 grey-white to pink petals; violet fruit ovoid-oblong, 1-5 cm long.

Syzygium cumini
Myrtaceae

Synonyms: *Myrtus cumini, Eugenia jambolanum, E. cumini*

Common names: Jambolan (En); pring bai (Cam); jamblang, duwet (Ins); va (Lao); jambulana, jambulan (Mal); thabyang-hpyoo (Bur); duhat, lomboi (Phi); wa, hakhiphae (Tha); vôi rung, trâm môc (Vie).

Description: A stout evergreen tree 10-20m (sometimes 30m) high, and 40-90cm in diameter, branching low with irregular crown spreading to about 12 m wide. Rough, dark grey bark on lower part, lighter grey and smooth higher up. Leaves opposite, entire, broadly obovate-elliptic to elliptic-oblong, 5-25 cm long and 2-10 cm wide with 1-3.5 cm long leaf stalk, cuneate or rounded at base, tip blunt, edges thin transparent, pinkish when young, later dark green above, faint turpentine smell when crushed. Flowers in 5-12 cm long panicles, usually on leafless branches, flowers small, fragrant with four grey-white to pink petals. Fruit ovoid-oblong, 1-5 cm long, dark violet and juicy with 0-5 green to brown seeds, up to 3.5 cm long inside.

Use: The subacid and astringent ripe fruit is eaten fresh or made into juice, jelly or wine. The leaves can be used as fodder. The abundant nectar of the flowers is a good source for bees to produce honey. The bark can be used for dyeing and also, together with seeds, has medicinal value. The tree is grown as shade tree, i.e. for coffee and the wood provides fair fuelwood.

Ecology: Grows on riverbanks in the tropical lowlands, best up to 600 m altitude. Above this height it does not fruit but can still grow up to about 1,800 m altitude and provide timber. Prefers 1,000 mm annual rain or more and a distinct dry season, but can withstand prolonged flooding.

Distribution: Native to subtropical Himalayas, India, Sri Lanka, Malesian region and Australia and presently cultivated throughout the tropics and subtropics.

References: Guzman et al (1986), Hensleigh & Holaway (1988), Verheij & Coronel (1992).

Key characteristics: Small; ever-green; branching low; dense wide-spread crown; stem mostly twisted at base; bark brown, smooth but furrowed; leaves oblong-lanceolate; flowers 5-10 cm wide, greenish-white; fruit round, to 5cm diameter, white-yellow, sometimes pink.

Syzygium jambos
Myrtaceae

Synonym: *Eugenia jambos*

Common names: Roseapple, malabar plum (En); châm'puu (Cam); jambu air mawar, jambu mawar, jambu kraton (Ins); chièng, kièng (Lao); jambu kelampok, jambu mawar (Mal); thabyu-thabye (Bur); chomphu-namdokmai, manomhom, yamu-panawa (Tha); lý, bô dào, roi (Vie).

Description: An evergreen tree up to 10 m high and 50 cm in diameter, often branching from low on the trunk and with dense wide spreading crown, stem cylindrical, sometimes quadrangular when young, mostly twisted at base. Bark brown, smooth, but furrowed. Leaves opposite, oblong-lanceolate, 9-26 cm long and 1.5-6cm wide, thin leathery, cuneate at base, pointed at tip, shiny dark green above, lighter green and glandular punctate underneath with 5-6, rarely 13 mm long leaf stalk. Inflorescence 5-10 cm long corymb, arising from tip of twigs or from leaf corners, 4-5(-10) flowered with large white to greenish-white, 5-10 cm wide 4-merous flowers with about 400 up to 4 cm long stamens. Fruit globose to ovoid, 2.5-5 cm in diameter, crowned by persistent 4-lobed calyx, whitish yellow, sometimes pink tainted, fragrant with yellow-pink flesh embedding 1-2(-4) sub-globose brown seeds, 1-1.5 cm in diameter.

Use: Fresh fruit is not so tasty and popular, but is cooked or preserved in various ways and can also be distilled to yield a high quality rose-water. Essential oil is extracted from the leaves for use in perfume production. The heavy and hard heartwood can be used for construction timber. The bark is used for dyeing and tanning. Several plant parts are used medicinally. Also used as ornamental tree.

Ecology: Tropical tree now being cultivated into the subtropics as well up to about 1,200 m altitude where climate is relatively wet. It grows on almost any slightly acid soil type including waterlogged.

Distribution: From its center of origin in Malesian region, it has spread throughout the tropics and has become widely naturalized.

References: Guzman et al (1986), Verheij & Coronel (1992).

Key characteristics: Small to medium sized; straight stem, often low branching; leaves opposite and big up to 38 cm long x 20 cm wide, thick leathery; red flowers on branches, red; fruits ellipsoid, 5-8 cm in diameter, dark red to yellowish (looks like an apple).

Syzygium malaccense
Myrtaceae

Synonyms: *Eugenia malaccensis, Jambosa malaccensis, E. domestica*

Common names: Malay apple (En); jambu bol (Ins, Mal); jambu merah (Mal); thabyo-thabyang (Bur); yanba, tersana, makopang-kalabaw (Phi); chomphu mamieo, chomphu saraek, chomphu daeng (Tha); cay dao, cay roi, dièu-dò (Vie).

Description: A tree in 5-20 m high with a straight stem and a broadly ovoid canopy, often branching near the base. Leaves opposite, elliptic-oblong, 15-38 cm long and 7-20 wide, thick leathery with 0.5-1.5 cm long thick leaf stalk, red when young. Inflorescence only on leafless twig parts, 1-12 flowered with 4-merous red flowers, 5-7 cm in diameter with numerous stamens. Fruit ellipsoid, 5-8 cm in diameter, crowned by the incurved calyx segments, dark red or purplish yellow or yellow white with juicy, white and fragrant flesh and one big brown seed.

Use: Primarily grown for its fruit which is eaten fresh or cooked in various ways. Wood is used for construction. Bark, leaves and roots provide traditional medicine with antibiotic activity.

Ecology: Native to wet tropical lowlands up to 1,200 m altitude. Needs year round water supply and prefers heavy soils.

Distribution: Native to southeast Asia and primarily found in Malaysia and Indonesia, but also grown in Burma, Thailand and Vietnam.

References: Verheij & Coronel (1992).

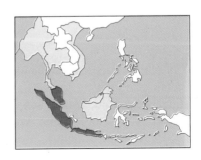

Key characteristics: Medium size; slow growing; evergreen; dense foliage; wide spreading round crown; bark grey brown, roughly fissured; leaves even-pinnate, 8-16 pairs of leaflets; flowers white and cream, with red-brown veins; pods light brown, curved, rounded, constricted between seeds.

Tamarindus indica

Leguminosae
(Caesalpinioideae)

Synonyms: *Tamarindus occidentalis, T. officinalis*

Common names: Tamarind, Indian tamarind (En); 'âm'pül, ampil, khoua me (Cam); asam, asam jawa, tambaring (Ins); khaam, mak kham (Lao); assam jawa (Mal); magyee, majee-pen (Bur); sampalok, kalamagi, salomagi (Phi); makham, bakham somkham (Tha); me, trai me (Vie).

Description: A medium sized slow growing but long lived evergreen tree, up to 30 m high. Trunk up to 2 m in diameter, branching low at 1-2 m from the base with greyish-brown rough fissured bark. Crown densely foliaged, widely spreading, rounded. Leaves alternate, even pinnately compound on leaf stalk up to 1.5 cm long, with 8-16 pairs of leaflets. Leaflets 1-3.5 cm long and 0.5-1cm wide. Flowers with 4 sepals and 5 petals, white and cream with red-brown stains. Fruit pods straight or curved with rounded ends, up to 14 cm long, light greyish or brown, constricted between seeds. Fruit "flesh" thick blackish-brown, seeds dark brown, very hard.

Use: Flesh of immature fruit pods is used for flavoring soups. Mature pods are eaten fresh or used in drinks, jams, candies, chutney, curries, ice cream, syrup or meat sauces. Oil and gum can be extracted from the seeds for food and industrial use. Leaves are used as soup flavour and for cattle forage or green manure. Wood is strong and durable and used for furniture, turnery, tool handles, toys, mortars, chopping blocks and also provides excellent fuel and charcoal.

Ecology: The tamarind grows within a wide range of soil and climatic conditions, but usually on sandy or clay soils up to about 1,000 m altitude or sometimes higher. Drought and wind resistant. In very wet conditions it does not flower.

Distribution: Native to tropical Africa and now planted in all tropical countries

References: Smitinand & Larsen (1984), Verheij & Coronel (1992).

Key characteristics: Straight trunk; low buttresses; deciduous large, simple leaves to 55 cm long, 37cm wide; inflorescence at branch tips, to 40 cm long; many small yellowish white flowers.

Tectona grandis   Verbenaceae

Synonym: *Tectona theka*

Common names: Teak (En); jati, deleg, kulidawa (Ins); sak (Lao); kyun (Bur); sak, mai-sak (Tha); caay teech, gias tij (Vie).

Description: A medium to large sized tree, 25-50 m tall with a straight trunk, 1-2.5 m in diameter, with dark greyish-brown, ridged bark and often low but-tresses. The deciduous leaves are simple, large, up to 55 cm long and 37 cm wide, short stalked, cuneate at base, ovate, round or obovately oblong with keeled midrib under-neath. The about 40 cm long inflorescence at tip of branches have numerous small yellowish-white flowers with pink stain, 3-6 mm long with 5-7 lobed calyx which eventually becomes inflated enclosing the fruit. Several forms have been distinguished primarily based on different leaf characters.

Use: An all-purpose timber tree used particularly for boat building, furniture, rails, docks, quays, piers and floodgates, house building, bridge construction, musical instruments and poles. Dye can be produced from young leaves and the bark of the root. Bark and wood also have various traditional medicinal uses.

Ecology: Found naturally in various types of tropical deciduous forests up to about 1,000 m on fertile, well drained soils, often associated with *Afzelia xylocarpa*, *Xylia*, *Terminalia* and *Lagerstroemia* spp. as well as bamboos.

Distribution: Native to southeast Asia, where it occurs naturally in Burma, Laos, Thailand and was introduced hundred years ago to Indonesia. Now cultivated in many countries both inside and outside the region, including China, Vietnam and the Philippines.

References: Hensleigh & Holaway (1988), Soerianegara & Lemmens (1994).

Key characteristics: Branches horizontal, in tiered whorls; leaves opposite, large, leathery, crowded towards branch tips; small flowers in small racemes from leaf base; fruit almond-like.

Terminalia catappa

Combretaceae

Synonym: *Terminalia procera*

Common names: Indian almond, tropical almond (En); ketapang (Ins,Mal); badan (Bur); talisae (Phi); bàng bièn (Vie).

Description: A medium sized tree up to 25m tall and 30cm in diameter with tiered whorls of horizontal branches, a flattened crown and slight buttresses. Leaves are opposite or sub-opposite, deciduous in dry climates, often crowded at the end of branches, 25 cm long, obovate, tapering to a narrow cordate base, leathery, shiny green, turning red or yellow before falling off. The inflorescence is a 6-18 cm long, narrow raceme from the leaf axil, with small greenish white, 5-6 mm large 5-merous flowers. Fruit an elliptical, slightly flattened drupe, about 5 cm long and 2.5 cm wide, first greenish, then light brown when ripe. The large stone (nut) about 3 cm long and 1cm wide and almond-like.

Use: The nut can be eaten raw or roasted and also contains extractable oils. The wood is used for light construction, boat building, furniture, veneer, posts, flooring and boxes and is also widely used for fuel. Leaves can be fed to livestock and some silkworms. Bark, roots, leaves and fruit rind contains tannins and also have several medicinal uses.

Ecology: Grows naturally in tropical beach forests and as a pioneer on denuded or disturbed lands up to 300 m altitude on sandy or limestone soils but is very adaptable.

Distribution: Native to East Indies and Oceania and now found throughout the tropics, including Burma, Thailand, Cambodia, Vietnam, Malaysia, Indonesia and the Philippines.

References: Guzman et al (1986); Hensleigh & Holaway (1988), National Research Council (1980).

Key characteristics: Small; branches in whorls of 5; leaves quite large with rounded 3-veined base; flowers and fruits on trunk and branches.

Trees and Fruits of Southeast Asia

Theobroma cacao

Sterculiaceae

Common names: Cacao (En); kakaaw (Cam); coklat (Ins); pokok coklat (Mal); kokoe (Bur); kho kho (Tha); cây ca cao (Vie).

Description: A scrub or small evergreen tree, 5-8 m tall (wild specimens can be up to 20 m) with a canopy about 4-5 m in diameter at 10 years age. Branches in whorls of 3-6. Leaves are semi-deciduous, 15-50 cm long and 4-15 cm wide, oblong ovate, acuminate with rounded base which is shortly 3 veined. Leaf stalk 1-10 cm, thickened at both ends. Yellow to white 5-merous flowers single or grouped on trunk and branches, about 1-1.5 cm in diameter. Fruit variable in shape, mostly ovoid, oblong, 10-30 cm long, usually pointed, wrinkled with 10 furrows of which 5 are prominent, yellow, green, red or purplish in color.

Use: Almost exclusively grown for the fruit which yields the cacao beans.

Ecology: Grows in warm, humid tropical habitats up to 700-1,000 m altitude, with uniform rain distribution of 1,000-5,000 mm annually, deep, well drained, fertile soil, rich in organic matter and not to acid.

Distribution: Native to the upper Amazonian region. It has been cultivated for several thousand years in its home area but is now also growing in most Asian countries with suitable climate.

References: Hensleigh & Holaway (1988) Purseglove (1974), Westphal & Jansen (1993).

Key characteristics: Crown open, widespread; sometimes buttresses; bark grey, fibrous, thinly flaked; leaves opposite, palmately compound; leaflets lance shaped; flowers bluish.

Vitex parviflora Verbenaceae

Common name: Molave (Phi).

Description: A medium sized deciduous tree up to 30 m tall and 1.5 m in diameter with an open wide-spreading crown and sometimes buttresses. The greyish ochre fibrous bark is smooth or thinly flaked. Leaves opposite, palmately compound on 9-11cm long leaf stalk, with 3-5 shiny and glabrous, lance-shaped, pointed leaflets, 4-15 cm long and 2.5-7 cm wide on 3-10 mm long stalks. Inflorescence is about 20 cm long pyramid-shaped panicle with many bluish flowers, 6-8 mm long. The fruits are small, round drupes, 5-10 mm in diameter, purple to black when ripe.

Use: The very strong and durable wood is used for house construction, ship building, railroad ties, plows and agricultural implements. Leaves can be fed to livestock.

Ecology: Grows naturally in open primary and secondary lowland tropical forests up to 700 m altitude, preferably on limestone or volcanic soils, in areas with a distinct dry season.

Distribution: Native to the Philippines. Also found in East Indonesia.

References: Hensleigh & Holaway (1988).

Key characteristics: Small; drooping branches; hairy zigzag-ging twigs with small spines; leaf hairy underneath, 3 prominent veins.

Ziziphus mauritiana

Rhamnaceae

Synonyms: *Rhamnus jujuba*, *Ziziphus jujuba*

Common names: Indian jujube (En); putrea (Cam); widara, dara, bidara (Ins); than (Lao); bidara, jujub, epal siam (Mal); zee-pen, zizidaw (Bur); manzanitas (Phi); phutsaa, ma tan (Tha); tao, tao nhuc (Vie).

Description: A bushy shrub or small tree up to 15 m high with drooping branches and hairy zigzagging twigs with small paired spines at leave bases (occasionally absent). Leaves alternate, simple, elliptic-ovate to oblong-elliptic, 2-9 cm long and 1.5-5 cm wide, entire or slightly crenate, glossy above, densely white haired below with 3 conspicuous longitudinal veins and 8-15 mm long leaf stalks. Inflorescence from leaf corners, 1-2 cm long with 7-20 yellowish 5-merous flowers, 2-3 mm across, weakly fragrant. The yellowish to reddish or blackish fruit is globose to ovoid, up to 6 x 4 cm when cultivated, smaller on wild trees, with glossy smooth or rough skin and white, juicy, weakly acid to sweet flesh.

Use: The fruit is eaten fresh, used to make drinks, candy or syrup or preserved by drying. Young leaves are cooked as vegetables or used as fodder. The tree is also used as a host tree for rearing lac insects, harvested to prepare shellac. The reddish wood is used for turnery, household items and implements.

Ecology: A hardy species tolerating extreme temperatures and dry conditions. Growing from sea level to about 1,000 m altitude where annual rainfall ranges between 125 to 2,000 mm, preferably on fairly light and deep soils, but tolerate even occasional waterlogging.

Distribution: Cultivated on small scale throughout the tropics and subtropics including all countries in Southeast Asia.

References: Verheij & Coronel (1992).

REFERENCES

Aksoernkoae, S., Maxwell, G.S., Havanond, S., Panichsuko, S. (1992): Plants in Mangroves. Chalongrat Co, Ltd., Bangkok.

Dransfield, J. & Manokaran, N. (1994): Plant Resources of South-East Asia, No. 6, Rattans. PROSEA, Bogor, Indonesia.

Dransfield, J. & Widjaja (1995): Plant Resources of South-East Asia - Bamboo. PROSEA, Bogor, Indonesia.

FAO (1992): Chemical Processing and Utilization of Acacia catechu Willd. FAO Regional Office for Asia & Pacific, Bangkok, Thailand.

Fong, C.H. & Hoi-Sen, Y. (1980): Malaysian Fruits in Colour. Tropical Press SDN. BHD. Kuala Lumpur, Malaysia.

F/RED (Forestry/Fuelwood Resarch and Development Project) (1992): Growing Multipurpose Trees on Small Farms. Winrock International, Bangkok, Thailand.

Guzman, E.; Umali, R.M. and Sotalbo, E.M. (1986): Guide to Philippine Flora and Fauna, Volume III. Natural Resources Management Center, Ministry of Natural Resources and University of the Philippines.

Hensleigh, T.E. and Holaway, B.K. (eds) (1988): Agroforestry Species for the Philippines. US Peace Corps, Manila, Philippines.

Ho, Pham-Hoang (undated): Botanical Book (In Vietnamese).

Hundley, H.G. and U Chit Ko Ko (1987): List of Trees, Schrubs, Herbs and Principal Climbers, etc. Recorded from Burma with Vernacular Names. Forest Department, Burma.

Kerala Forest Research Institute (1985): Dipterocarps of South Asia. RAPA Monograph 1985/4. FAO, Bangkok, Thailand. Little, Elbert L. (- undated): Common Fuelwood Crops - A Handbook for Their Identification. Communi-Tech Associates, Morgantown, West Virginia, USA.

Mabberley, D.J. (1993): The Plant Book. Cambridge University Press.

MacDicken, Kenneth G. (1988): Nitrogen Fixing Trees for Wastelands. RAPA Publication 1988/9, FAO, Bangkok.

MacDicken, Kenneth G. (1994): Selection and Management of Nitrogen-fixing Trees. FAO/Winrock International.

Muséum National D'histoire Naturelle (1960-94): Flore du Cambodge du Laos et du Viêtnam. Vol 1-27. Paris, France.

National research council (1992): Neem - A tree for solving global problems. National Academy Press.

Purseglove, J.W. (1974): Tropical Crops - Dicotyledons. Longman, Essex, England.

—"— (1985): Tropical Crops - Monocotyledons. Longman Inc, New York.

Smitinand T. and Larsen, K. (eds) (1981): Flora of Thailand, volume two. TISTR Press, Bangkok, Thailand.

Smitinand T. and Larsen, K. (eds) (1984): Flora of Thailand, volume four, part one, Leguminosae - Caesalpinioideae. The Forest Herbarium, Royal Forest Department.

Smitinand T. and Larsen, K. (eds) (1985): Flora of Thailand, volume four, part two, Leguminosae - Mimosoideae. The Forest Herbarium, Royal Forest Department. TISTR Press, Bangkok, Thailand.

Smitinand T. and Larsen, K. (eds) (1987): Flora of Thailand, volume five, part one. The Forest Herbarium, Royal Forest Department. TISTR Press, Bangkok, Thailand.

Soerianegara, I. and Lemmens, R.H.M.J. (Eds) (1994): Timber trees: Major commercial timbers. Plant Resources of South-East Asia, No 5 (1). PROSEA, Bogor, Indonesia.

Storrs, Adrian and Jimmy (1990): Trees and shrubs of Nepal and the Himalays. Pilgrims Book House, Kathmandu, Nepal.

Verheij, E.W.M. and Coronel, R.E. (Eds) (1992): Edible fruits and nuts. Plant Resources of South-East Asia, No. 2. PROSEA, Bogor, Indonesia.

Westphal, E. & Jansen, P.C.M. (1993): Plant Resources of South-East Asia - A selection. PROSEA, Bogor, Indonesia.

Whitmore, T.C. (1979): Palms of Malaya. Oxford University Press, Malaysia.

Whitmore, T.C. & Ng, F.S.P. (eds) (1978): Tree Flora of Malaya, Vol. 3, Malayan Forest Records No. 26. Longman Malaysia SDN Berhad, Kuala Lumpur.

INDEX OF SCIENTIFIC AND COMMON NAMES

Trees and Fruits of Southeast Asia

Trees and Fruits of Southeast Asia

Where information was available local deviation has been indicated. Most species are cultivated outside their natural habitat and the actual timing of rain and sunshine in a given year will affect the exact period when fruits mature.

English	Species	Local names	Harvest season	Comments
Coconut	*Cocos nucifera*	kelapa (Ins, Mal); on, makun (Bur); niog (Phi); mapraaw (Tha); dùa (Vie).	Year round	
Banana	*Musa spp.*	cheek nam' vaa (Cam); pisang (Ins, Mal); kwàyz (Lao); nget pyo thee (Bur); gluay (Tha); chuôí (Vie).	Year round	
Bael	*Aegle marmelos*	bnau (Cam); maja, maja batuh (Ins); toum (Lao); bilak, bila, bel (Mal); opesheet, ohshit (Bur); matum, tum, ma pin (Tha); trái mam (Vie).	Dry season	
Cashew	*Anacardium occidentale*	svaay chantii (Cam); jambu monyet, jambu mede (Ins); Gajus, jambu monyet (Mal); thiho thayet si (Bur); kasoy, balubad, balogo (Phi); mamuang himmaphan, yaruang, mamuang letlor (Tha); dào lôn hôt,cay diêù (Vie).	March-June	Philippines
Guayabano, soursop	*Annona muricata*	tiep barang (Cam); sirsak, nangka belanda (Ins); khan thalot, khièp thét (Lao); durian belanda (Mal); duyin-awza (Bur); guayabano (Phi); thurian thet, rian nam (Tha); mang câu xiêm (Vie).	May-Aug	Philippines, year round in tropics
Sugar apple, sweetsop, Custard apple	*Annona squamosa*	tiep baay, tiep srok (Cam); Sirkaja, sarikaja, atis (Ins); khieb (Lao); nona sri kaya, buah nona, sri kaya (Mal); awza (Bur); atis (Phi); noina, makkhiap, lanang (Tha); na, mang câu ta (Vie).	June-Sept	Philippines
Breadfruit	*Artocarpus altillis*	sakéé, khnaôr samloo (Cam); sukun (seedless), kelur, timbul (seeded) (Ins, Mal); paung-thi (Bur); rimas (seedless), kamansii	May-Aug	Philippines, year round near equator

		(seeded) (Phi); sa-ke (seed-less), khanun-sampalor (Tha); sakê (Vie).		
 Jackfruit	*Artocarpus heterophyllus*	khnaor (Cam); nangka (Ins,Mal); miiz, miiz hnang (Lao); peignai (Bur); langka (Phi); khanon, makmi, banun (Tha); mit (Vie).	Year round, but mainly Jan-May March-Aug Apr-Aug & Sept-Dec	Thailand Philippines Malaysia
 Cempedak	*Artocarpus integer*	chempedak, campedak, baroh (Ins); chempedak [cultivated], bankong [wild] (Mal); sonekadat (Bur); champada (Tha); mit tó nù (Vie).	June-Aug Sept-Dec	Malaysia Java, Indonesia
 Billimi	*Averrhoa bilimbi*	tralong tong (Cam); belim-bing asam, belimbing wuluh, belimbing buluk (Ins, Mal); tayok-zaungya (Bur); kamias, iba (Phi); taling pling (Tha); khe tau (Vie).	Year round	
 Carambola, star fruits	*Averrhoa carambola*	spo (Cam); fuand (Lao); belimbing manis (Mal, Ins); zaung-ya (Bur); Balimbing (Phi); ma fuang (Tha); khe (Vie).	June-Aug Year round	Philippines Thailand
Kapundung	*Baccaurea racemosa*	mente, kepundung (Ins, Mal); bencoy (Ins); jinteh merah.(Mal).	Aug-Sept	Malaysia
 Burmese grape	*Baccaurea ramiflora*	phnkiew (Cam); mafai setam-bun, tajam molek (Ins); f'ai (Lao); pupor, tampoi, tempui (Mal); kanazo (Bur); mafai, omfai, hamkang (Tha); giau gia dat, giau tien, dzau mien dzu'ó'i (Vie).	Aug-Sept	Malaysia
 Gandaria	*Bouea macrophylla*	ramania, gandaria (Ins); kundang, rembunia, setar (Mal); ma praang, somprang (Tha).	March-June	Indonesia
 Papaya, pawpaw	*Carica papaya*	ihong, doeum lahong (Cam); papaya, gedang, kates (Ins); houng (Lao); papaya, betek, ketalah (Mal); thimbaw (Bur); papaya, kapaya, lapaya (Phi); malakor, loko, ma kuai thet (Tha); du du (Vie).	Year round	
 Cainito, starapple	*Chrysophyllum cainito*	sawo ijo, sawo hejo, sawo kadu (Ins); sawo duren, pepulut (Mal); hnin-thagya (Bur); caimito (Phi); chicle durian (Sin); sataa appoen (Tha); vú-sùe (Vie).	Jan-April July	Philippines Indonesia

Lime, sour lime	*Citrus aurantiifolia*	krôôch chmaa muul (Cam); jeruk nipis, jeruk pecel (Ins); naaw (Lao); limau ni-pis, limau asam (Mal); dayap (Phi); som manao, manao (Tha); chanh ta (Vie).	Almost year round	
Mauritius papeda	*Citrus hystrix*	krauch soeuch (Cam); jeruk perut, limo purut (Ins); 'khi 'hout (Lao); limau purut (Mal); shouk-pote (Bur); kabuyau, kulubut, kolobot (Phi); ma kruut (Tha); trúc (Vie).	Almost year round	
Pummelo, shaddock	*Citrus maxima*	krôôch thlông (Cam); jeruk besar, jeruk bali (Ins); kiéngz s'aangz, ph'uk, sômz 'ôô (Lao); jambua, limau betawi, limau bali (Mal); shouk-ton-oh, kywegaw (Bur); som-o, ma-o (Tha); bu'o'i (Vie).	Nov-Jan Aug-Nov	Philippines Thailand
Mandarin, tangerine	*Citrus reticulata*	krauch kvich (Cam); jeruk ke-prok, jeruk jepun, jeruk maseh (Ins); som hot, som lot, liou (Lao); limau langkat, limau kupas, limau wangkas (Mal); leinmaw (Bur); som khieo waan, som saenthong, ma baang (Tha); cam sành, cay quit (Vie).	Almost year round	
Sweet orange	*Citrus sinensis*	krôôch pôôsat (Cam); jeruk manis (Ins); kièngz (Lao); limau manis, chula, choreng (Mal); thung chin-thi (Bur); kahel (Phi); somkliang, somtra (Tha); cam (Vie).	Nov-Feb	Philippines
Longan	*Dimocarpus longan*	mien (Cam); lengkeng (Ins, Mal); lam nhai (Lao); kyet mouk (Bur); lamyai pa (Tha); nhan (Vie). -ssp. longan var. obtusus: lamyai khruer, lamyai tao (Tha). -ssp. malesianus var. malesianus: Mata kucing (peninsular Mal and Sabah); isau, sau, kakus (Sarawak); buku, ihau, meduru (Ins).	Aug-Sept	Thailand
Durian	*Durio zibethinus*	thu-réén (Cam); duren, ambetan, kadu (Ins); thurièn (Lao); thurian, rian (Tha); saù riêng (Vie).	June-Aug July-Oct May-Aug	Peninsular Malaysia Philippines Thailand
Mangosteen	*Garcinia mangostana*	manggis (Ins, Mal); mankhud (Lao); mingut (Bur); mang-gustan,(Phi); Mangkhut (Tha); cay mang cut (Vie).	Aug-Oct until Nov	Philippines Indonesia

Main harvest season

Langsat	*Lansium domesticum*	langsat, duku, kokosan (Ins, Mal); langsat, duku (Bur); lansones, buahan (Phi); langsat, duku, longkong (Tha); bòn-bon (Vie).	July-Oct June-Feb	Thailand and Philippines Malaysia
Lychee, litchi	*Litchi chinensis*	kuléén (Cam); litsi, klèng-keng, kalèngkeng (Ins); ngèèw (Lao); laici, keleng-kang (Mal); kyet-mouk, lin chi, lam yai (Bur); linchee, lit-chi, see raaman (Tha); vai, cay vai, tu hú (Vie).	April-Jun Oct-Feb	Thailand Indonesia
Macademia nut	*Macadamia integrifolia*	Macademia nut (En).	Oct-Dec	In its original habitat in Australia
	Mangifera altissima	Medang kok, membacang (Ins); paho, pahutan, pangamangaen (Phi).	Year round	
Horse mango	*Mangifera foetida*	svaay sââ (Cam); bachang, limus, asem hambawang (Ins); bachang, machang, pahu (Mal); thayet-poh, lamut (Bur); xoài hôi (Vie).	Aug-Jan	Malaysia and Indonesia
Mango	*Mangifera indica*	svaay (Cam); mangga, mempelam, ampelam (Ins, Mal); mwàngx (Lao); tharyetthi (Bur); mangga, paho, mango (Phi); xoài (Vie).	April-June Jan-May	Philippines Thailand
	Manilkara kaukii	Sawo kecik, kayu sawo, sabo (Ins); sawah, sawai, sawau (Mal); lamut-thai, lamut-sida (Tha); gang-néo (Vie).	Aug-Sept	Bali, Indonesia
Sapodilla, noseberry	*Manilkara zapota*	lomut (Cam); sawo manila, ciku, sawo londo (Ins); lamud (Lao); ciku (Mal); chico (Phi); lamut, lamut-farang (Tha); xabôchê, hông xiêm, tam lu'c (Vie).	April-Sept Sept-Dec	Philippines Thailand
Rambutan	*Nephelium lappaceum*	saaw maaw, ser mon (Cam); rambutan (Ins, Mal,Phi); usan (Phi); ngoh, phruan (Tha); chôm chôm, vai thiêù (Vie).	July-Sept May-Sept	Philippines Thailand
Avocado, alligator pear	*Persea americana*	avôkaa (Cam); adpukat, avokad (Ins); avokado, apukado (Mal); htaw bat (Bur); awokado (Tha); bo', lê daù (Vie).	May-Aug	Philippines

Otaheite gooseberry	*Phyllanthus acidus*	ceremoi, cereme (Ins); cherma(Mal); thinbo-zihpyoo (Bur); iba, bang-kiling, karmay (Phi); ma-yom (Tha); chùm ruôt (Vie).	Sept-Oct	Bali, Indonesia
Guava	*Psidium guajava*	jambu batu, biyabas (Bru); trapaek sruk (Cam); jambu biji, jambu klotok (Ins); sida (Lao); jambu biji, jambu kampuchia, jambu berase (Mal); Guava, bayabas, (Phi); malakapen (Bur); ma kuai, ma-man, farang (Tha); Oi (Vie).	July-Sept	Philippines. (Almost year round with proper management, Thailand.)
Pomegranate	*Punica granatum*	totum (Cam); delima (Ins, Mal); phiilaa (Lao); salebin, talebin, thale (Bur); granada (Phi); thapthim (C.Tha); phila (N.E. Tha); bakoh (N.Tha); lu'u, thap lu'u (Vie).	Aug-Oct	Several annual bearings in the tropics
Santol, kechapi	*Sandoricum koetjape*	kôm piing riëch (Cam); kecapi, ketuat, sentul (Ins, Mal); toongz (Lao); thitto (Bur); kra thon, sa thon (Tha); sâú (Vie).	June-Aug	Philippines
Ambarella, otaheite apple	*Spondias cytherea*	great hog plum (En); mokak (Cam); kedondong manis (Ins); kook hvaan (Lao); kedondong (Mal); gway (Bur); hevi (Phi); makok-farang (Tha); cóc (Vie).	Jan-April	Java
Water apple, bell fruit	*Syzygium aqueum*	jambu air, jambu air mawar (Ins, Mal); tambis (Phi); machomphu-pa (Tha).	Almost year round	No regular growth cycle
Wax jambu, java apple	*Syzygium samarangense*	jambu semarang, jambu klampok (Ins); jambu air mawar (Mal); makopa (Phi); chomphu-kaemmaem, chomphu-khieo, chomphu-nak (Tha); man, roi (Vie).	May-July	Philippines
Jambolan	*Syzygium cumini*	pring bai (Cam); jamblang, duwet (Ins); va (Lao); jambulana, jambulan (Mal); thabyang-hpyoo (Bur); duhat, lomboi (Phi); wa, hakhiphae (Tha); vôi rung, trâm môc (Vie).	April-June	Philippines

Main harvest season   231

Roseapple	*Syzygium jambos*	châm'puu (Cam); jambu air mawar, jambu mawar, jambu kraton (Ins); chièng, kièng (Lao); jambu kelampok, jambu mawar (Mal); thabyu-thabye (Bur); chomphu-namdokmai, manomhom, yamu-panawa (Tha); lý, bô dào, roi (Vie).	June-Sept	Very depen-dant on location
Malay apple	*Syzygium malaccense*	jambu bol (Ins, Mal); jambu merah (Mal); thabyo-thabyang (Bur); yanba, tersana, makopang-kalabaw (Phi); chomphu mamieo, chomphu saraek, chomphu daeng (Tha); cay dao, cay roi, dièu-dò (Vie).	Almost year round	No regular growth cycle
Tamarind	*Tamarindus indica*	Indian tamarind (En); 'âm'pül, ampil, khoua me (Cam); asam, asam jawa, tambaring (Ins); khaam, mak kham (Lao); assam jawa (Mal); magyee, majee-pen (Bur); sampalok, kalamagi, salomagi (Phi); makham, bakham somkham (Tha); me, trai me (Vie).	July-Feb	First in the Philippines, later in Thailand
Indian jujube	*Ziziphus mauritiana*	putrea (Cam); widara, dara, bidara (Ins); than (Lao); bidara, jujub, epal siam (Mal); zee-pen, zizidaw (Bur); manzanitas (Phi); phutsaa, ma tan (Tha); tao, tao nhuc (Vie).	Dry season	

PESTICIDES AND FRUITS

As fruit growing has become more commercialized the size of plantations has increased, the number of species grown in one plantation has decreased and the distances (hence time) fruits are transported has increased. Moreover, as fruits nowadays are often passed from trader to trader, from one storage site to another, the same consignment may be treated with pesticides several times thus increasing the residue of chemicals.

Because of these changes in the pattern of cultivation and marketing, the use of various chemicals has generally been on the rise. This includes waxy, glossy coverings to improve appearance, chemicals to induce ripening because fruits are picked before they mature and in particular fungicides to preserve the fruits during extensive transport. In addition, colouring agents may be used to improve the appearance of the fruits In Thailand, for example, lamud (sapodilla) may be dye-coated with a strong red-brown colour to make it more appealing.

As a consumer, it is very hard to know which chemicals have been applied and in what amounts, since most of these chemicals leave no trace in smell and taste of the fruits. Regulations for pesticide use vary between countries and in many places they are not enforced in practice. Especially in developing countries uneducated personnel often apply many of these pesticides in a very haphazard manner. They therefore constitute a major problem both to those who do the spraying and especially to those of us who enjoy the taste of fresh fruits on a regular basis.

How to avoid this problem then? Well, most people are not able to grow their own fruit and hence control their treatment. But if you are, why don't you plant some appropriate fruit trees and enjoy the pleasure of nurturing and eating you own, unsprayed, fruit production? Thais traditionally plant papaya, mango, mayoom or gooseberry, banana, jackfruit, tamarind and guava in their yards.

Consumer organizations are a strong force in some countries and are able to have some influence on pesticide use, but if this is not the case in your country you may consider being the one to initiate or work for such a pressure group! In Malaysia, for example, the pro-consumer magazine Utusan Konsumer regularly reports on pesticides and related problems, and in Thailand the monthly Organic Agriculture does the same.

One way to limit the risk of excessive pesticide intake is to use the fruit calendar in this book. If you stick to fruits of your own area and only eat them in their natural fruiting season you are a far better off, since they will be fresher and have less transport and storage time behind them. Hence the need for pesticides has been reduced. In general, imported fruit should be avoided, as they are often heavily treated with pesticides, fungicides and rodenticides.

Apart from eating fruits in their natural season only, the following simple precautions may be helpful to the fruit-lover to reduce pesticide intake:

- Be selective when buying fruit. The thoroughly yellow colour of mangoes might come from the gas fumigating process. It is said that fruit that ripens naturally will still have some green parts. The bright red-brown colour of sapodilla is not natural; the pale brown is. The general rule is to be careful with unblemished and flawless fruit. They are often too good to be true!

- Cleaning thoroughly in water is the best treatment. Scrubbing in water and soaking in water can help reduce up to 50 per cent of residues. Soaking in water with a tablespoon of bicarbonate or soda in 20 litres of water for 15 minutes may reduce a good amount of chemicals, but unfortunately also some vitamin A. Soaking grapes in a mixture of vinegar and water can get rid of some chemicals.

- Peeling may remove all residues if they are confined to the surface. Some chemicals, however, can be absorbed in the fruit flesh and removal is virtually impossible.

- Storing fruit in the refrigerator can also help reduce chemicals. For example, keeping grapes in the fridge for seven days can reduce 65 per cent of the chemical residues.